Fundholding: a practice guide

Second Edition

Edited by
Antoinette Pirie and
Mercedes Kelly-Madden

RADCLIFFE MEDICAL PRESS
OXFORD and NEW YORK

© 1994 Radcliffe Medical Press Ltd
15 Kings Meadow, Ferry Hinksey Road, Oxford OX2 0DP

141 Fifth Avenue, Suite N, New York, NY 10010, USA

British Library Cataloguing in Publication Data

A cataloguing record for this book is available from the British Library

ISBN 1 85775 040 3

Typeset by Acorn Bookwork, Salisbury, Wiltshire
Printed and bound in Great Britain by
Biddles Ltd, Guildford and King's Lynn

Contents

Authors

Nicola Amery
Hospital Director, Godden Green Clinic and Business Manager for Cygnet Health Care. Formerly Fundholding Development Manager, VAMP Health Ltd

Andrew Burnett
Director of Primary Care Development, Kent Family Health Services Authority

Jeremy Harris
General Practitioner, Kingston upon Thames

Lynne Hobden Clarke
Practice Manager, Chalfont St Peter and Editorial Adviser, *Practice Manager*

Ian Howarth
Development Manager, Lincolnshire Family Health Services Authority

Mercedes Kelly-Madden
Management Consultant for General Practice Fundholding Consultancy. Formerly Fundholding Manager, East Sussex Family Health Services Authority and Fundholding Adviser to South East Thames Regional Health Authority

Antoinette Pirie
Medical Director, West Herts NHS Trust

Laurence Slavin
Partner, Ramsay Brown and Partners, Chartered Accountants

Peter Smith
General Practitioner and Medical Director of Kingston & Richmond Multifund

Barry Strickland-Hodge
Prescribing Adviser, Kingston & Richmond Multifund

David Tod
President, National Association of Fundholding Practices. Senior partner, fundholding practice, London

Ian Walker
Managing Director, Healthcare Consultancy Services Ltd. Formerly Contracts Manager, Hertfordshire Family Health Services Authority

Tim Young
Partner, Bevan Ashford, Solicitors, Bristol

1

Introduction

Antoinette Pirie

In January 1989 the Government published a White Paper on the future of the National Health Service (NHS), *Working for Patients*. The proposals set out represented some of the most radical changes to the NHS since its creation over 40 years ago.

A central element of the change programme is the general practice fundholding initiative. The White Paper recognized that general practitioners (GPs) were uniquely placed to improve patients' choice of good quality services because of their relationships with patients and hospitals. The principal aim of the GP fundholding scheme is to build on this unique situation so that patients can benefit further. It calls for the development of a management infrastructure which enables larger practices to take control of expenditure on certain services delivered to their patients. The legislation has now been passed as the National Health Service and Community Care Act 1990.

The stated objectives of the practice budget for general medical practitioners are:

- to improve the quality of services on offer to patients by GPs

- to help GPs develop their practices for the benefit of their patients

- to allow GPs greater control over the use of resources for their patients

- to encourage hospitals to be more responsive to the needs of GPs and their patients.

These aims complement the general thrust of *Working for Patients* which set out to:

- extend patient choice
- delegate responsibility to where services are provided
- secure the best value for money.

The overhaul mapped out for the NHS has several distinguishing attributes when compared to the financial and organizational structure of the NHS pre 1991:

- it offers an internal market where the provider and the purchaser of the care are separated
- it offers consumers a choice among several competing providers
- it is based on a fixed budget that encompasses both the primary and secondary care sectors
- the individual GP is offered financial incentives to provide and co-ordinate care with an eye towards resource management.

All four of these characteristics can be expected to improve efficiency. They will also provide certain incentives to improve the quality of care.

The initiative has called for a redefinition of roles and responsibilities by those involved in the delivery of health care and examination of the new working relationships that are required. To ensure success in a change exercise of this scale it has been important to ensure that:

- patients remain secure in the knowledge that health care will continue and improve
- the transitional period between existing and new arrangements is carefully planned
- the skills and expertise required to effect the change are identified and either developed or acquired.

The history of primary care as a fragmented service provided by independent contractors on the one hand, and salaried and accountable staff on the other, has ensured a lack of a coherent organizational and policy framework for developing a high quality, integrated service. The need to rationalize shared services and expand the contribution of the primary care sector in acute care reinforces the trend towards an expanded primary care service. All this has taken place within the context of an increased planning and management role for Family Health Services Authorities (FHSAs) and a White Paper which made it clear that the role of GPs is to be extended. The shifting boundaries created by the current changes within the NHS call for greater collaboration between the agencies involved in the delivery of primary health - namely FHSAs, District Health Authorities (DHAs) and independent contractors.

Realigning the boundaries between acute care and primary care is on the agenda for a number of reasons. The acute sector is increasingly concerned with maximizing throughput, reducing costs and promoting efficiency in the use of resources. In parallel with this many GPs have been keen to enhance links with the acute sector. Users of the service think that care should be provided, as far as possible, in a community setting, this is also in line with the philosophy of the World Health Organization. In practical terms this has been translated into:

- increasing the range of community-based staff to whom GPs can directly refer and work with as part of the primary care team

- increasing GP access to hospital diagnostic and therapeutic services

- increasing management of chronic disease by GPs, eg diabetes and asthma

- providing an increasing number of specialist services in a community setting.

The White Paper recognized that GPs were uniquely placed to improve patients' choice of good quality services because of their relationships with patients and hospitals. The principal aim of the GP fundholding scheme is to build on this situation so that patients can benefit further.

Fundholding focuses on restructuring aspects of primary care and can be viewed as a lever for improving care in the hospital sector - using a bottom-up approach to effect changes throughout the entire health care system. Fundholding practices will be making a major contribution to the overall aim of generating increased efficiency in the hospital system in the interests of patients.

Managing resources more efficiently with the goal of providing the most effective care possible within the available budget is as vital to both the patient's and society's well-being as any task now facing GPs. Who else is better able to decide whether a particular patient group is best served by more preventive, primary, secondary or long-term care? None of these are easy decisions, but with appropriate consumer input and with their knowledge of both the practice population and individual patients, GPs are in a unique position to play this role. General practice funds are a practical acknowledgement that GPs are the gatekeepers of the NHS.

2

The General Practice Fundholding Initiative

Antoinette Pirie

The general practice fundholding initiative is a key component of the changes in the NHS and in this chapter some of the main elements of the initiative are addressed. Whilst appreciating the political and philosophical arguments that surround the concept, it is not the intention to enter into that debate here, but rather to present the terms and scope of the scheme.

Which practices are eligible to become fundholders?

Initially only those practices with at least 11,000 patients were to be considered but this has now been relaxed to 9,000. Smaller practices have been allowed to group together in order to opt for GP practice budgets.

The limit has been relaxed in the third wave to include practices with fewer patients.

Practices have to demonstrate the ability to manage a budget. They need to have adequate administrative support and computer and information systems in place.

FHSAs are responsible for the fundholding GPs' contracts and monitor expenditure against the budget. The practices within the scheme however, will receive their budgets directly from the relevant Regional Health Authority (RHA). There is close co-operation between FHSAs and RHAs in agreeing budgets with the participating practices.

Initially practice funds were determined on a case-by-case basis taking into account the different expenditure components contributing to the total budget. A weighted capitation formula, which reflects the actual need of a given population of patients will be used for future allocation.

What is the scope of the budget?

Out of a determined annual budget the following expenditures must be covered:

- all practice team staff costs and practice accommodation costs which are at present directly reimbursed under the standard GP contract

- all expenses incurred during management of the fund and other costs associated with participation in the fundholding initiative itself

- all drugs prescribed and dispensed

- any diagnostic investigation of patients or specimens ordered or performed by the GP (or hospital consultant, if in context)

- initial and continuing out-patient services delivered by hospital-based staff

- costs relating to a defined group of surgical in-patient and day-case treatment – the list covers most elective procedures (*see* Appendix). Emergency admissions and medical admissions are excluded

- costs relating to direct access services – physiotherapy, speech therapy and occupational therapy, dietetics and chiropody.

- health visiting and community nursing, elements of mental health and learning disabilities services.

This will increase the range of services under the control of fundholders.

A key element of fundholding is that provider units will provide services to participating practices on a selectively contracted basis. Each fundholding practice will negotiate its own contracts for specific services with directly managed units (DMUs), self-governing trust hospitals and/or private hospitals. There are considered to be three main types of possible contractual arrangement:

1. **Block contracts** will cover the provision of a defined block of services in return for an annual fee

2. **Cost and volume contracts** – providers will receive a defined sum for the provision of a baseline level of activity. Beyond that level, payment will be on a cost per case basis

3. **Limited volume contracts** – payments for a defined volume of cases.

4. **Cost per case contracts** will be payments on the basis of a sum for each case treated.

It will be necessary for practices participating in the scheme to have contractual arrangements in place prior to becoming fund holders to ensure continuity of care.

Before the level of the budget can be agreed both the practice and the RHA will need information on current referral rates and use of hospital facilities ie laboratory and X-ray requests, attendance at outpatient departments, and surgical inpatient treatment rates. Similar information will be required during the year to monitor expenditure against the budget.

Hospitals have developed profiles of patient costs to be able to attach costs to individual treatments and procedures. They are in a position to price their services and the information will be used to permit contract funding of services.

What services are not covered in the budget?

A series of services are excluded from the budget and will be borne by the relevant Health Authority. These include:

- accident and emergency services
- hospital and consultant costs associated with medical cases and non-elective surgery

- maternity services
- certain preventive and screening tests.

There will be a limit to the practice's financial responsibility of £5,000 of hospital treatment per person per year. The RHA will also rescue a practice that overspends its budget by up to 5%. Expenditures in excess of this level would, however, lead to a thorough audit and the possibility of having the fund withdrawn.

3

The Decision

David Tod

There are now 1,200 fundholding practices, looking after some 25% of the population of England and Wales. Of those which started in 1991, only two or three practices have withdrawn from the scheme and hundreds more are preparing for the fourth wave entry in 1994.

Fundholding's impact on patient care is being felt at every level within the National Health Service. At the local level, innovation among fundholders has become a byword for efficient services at a reduced cost. Services which practices have introduced include physiotherapy, chiropody, endoscopy, counselling, ECG and various diagnostic services.

Increasingly, specialist out-patient services are being developed (including orthopaedics, rheumatology, dermatology, gynaecology and ophthalmology), with specialist advice, consultation and follow-up taking place in conjunction with the fundholder and on site.

Ultrasound technology is being introduced, and as more sophisticated equipment becomes available and groups of practices come together to form consortia or multi-fund groups, there is no reason why such groupings should not develop their own locality centre for investigation, using X-ray equipment and providing facilities for endoscopy, colposcopy, day surgery and other procedures currently being provided in hospital out-patient clinics.

Fundholding practices are increasingly coming together within districts to discuss such arrangements and developments, and over the next few years the growth pattern of fundholding practices will become more like the poly-clinic in the USA and other Western countries. As fundholding GPs develop their interests and co-operate with their local consultants, their level of expertise will develop and patients will benefit from being diagnosed and treated more efficiently in their own locality and by a family doctor who still retains their care.

The benefits arising from these changes are not just for patient and doctor but also for the hospital service, which will be able to concentrate on those areas requiring high technology or complex procedures of a specialist nature beyond the scope of the new-style practice.

Similarly, the taxpayer will benefit in that these service developments will provide savings both direct, due to a more cost-effective local service, and indirect, due to patient time being saved on travelling or waiting for hospital-based activity.

The fund

Fundholding allows the practice to purchase, on behalf of its patients, various forms of service. These include:

- investigatory procedures
- out-patient referrals
- non-emergency surgery
- community nursing and health visiting services
- chiropody
- non-emergency mental health services which includes counselling and community psychiatric nursing
- services for people with learning disabilities
- physiotherapy.

The fund also includes money for the:

- staff budget
- management allowance (both of which are agreed with the Regional Health Authority [or FHSA])
- purchasing budget.

Because of this 'bottom-up' approach most fundholding practices have been able to purchase these services at a cheaper cost than local Health Authorities. Such savings have been used for the purchase of equipment, improvement of premises and provision of additional patient care. Much has been said about the large savings made by a few practices, these were usually the result of insufficient data from provider units, increased practice efficiency and sometimes substantial use of the private sector by patients. As fundholding moves forward, onto a capitation-based footing, some of these variations will disappear.

Practice prescribing

The introduction of a budget for prescribing costs into fundholding has given a new twist to the discussion over the drugs bill. Fundholders have already become greater users of generic drugs, they are more discriminating over new expensive drugs and have less of a percentage increase on their drugs bill than their non-fundholding colleagues.

PACT (Prescribing Conditions and Costs) data and various formularies help practices to develop and discuss sensible prescribing and at the same time to discuss with the local FHSA pharmaceutical advisers the relative merits and costs of similar preparations.

Practice staff budget

One of the benefits of fundholding has been the decision to include a practice staff budget within the fund and to be able to transfer any deficit across to or from the prescribing or hospital activity budgets. At the same time the fundholding practice can move staff or change their work patterns without recourse to the FHSA, provided there is no overall change in expenditure.

Mechanism for control

In any system of health care provision where public monies are being spent, systems must be introduced which can inspect, evaluate and if necessary be changed or updated.

So far the administrative costs of fundholding have been the cost of computer equipment and software, the management allowance and the maintenance costs. On average these are about £50,000 p.a. per fundholding practice and about 3–5% therefore of the total fundholding budget. This cost compares favourably with the total NHS management costs of about 9%. From these figures it will be obvious that the benefit of introducing the computerization programme, the savings made by fundholders and the entrepreneurial services being developed for their patients far outweigh any financial consideration or implied critisism.

However, each Regional Health Authority (or FHSA), being responsible for the overall management of fundholders, has to make sure that the computer equipment used is appropriate, that the management is competent, that the data quality is of high standard, that contracts with providers are appropriate and that every fundholding practice is generating its own material on time.

The quality of data being provided by fundholders is higher than that produced by most provider units and can, at times, lead to difficulties over agreement on end-of-year figures because of provider's rather than fundholders' inefficiencies.

Contracts

Fundholders are now becoming expert at contracting with provider services and, are beginning to insert conditions concerning quality issues. These are mostly concentrated on issues such as waiting lists, waiting times, transport services for the elderly or children, but discussions are starting on re-admission rates and repeat consultations etc.

Increasingly, contracts are being developed on a cost per case or limited volume basis and this is to the benefit of both the fundholder's budget and the provider's. At the same time, consultant services within the surgery are being introduced as part of the service contract. Fundholders are also developing contracts with providers some distance away, particularly if the service is of high quality at lower cost and, similarly, making use of any spare capacity or under-use of local private hospitals. This is particularly useful for the reduction of long waiting lists or the provision of services such as physiotherapy and pathology.

Fundholders are also using the option of referring patients to homoeopathic providers.

A relatively new development, is awarding contracts for services within the practice, such as ultrasound and counselling/psychotherapy either an an alternative, or in addition to, existing local psychiatric services. It is becoming important for these services to be assessed for cost-effectiveness and quality.

Impact of fundholding

It is self-evident, therefore, that the impact on patient care has been considerable, but what about the impact on the rest of the NHS? In some areas more than 50% of the population is covered by fundholding practices; what effect is this having?

Fundholding practices are beginning to question not just administrative quality issues such as appointment delays, long waiting times and discharge letters, but also clinical data and activity.

Some consultants over-investigate or retain patients in beds too long and often delegate too much to their juniors. Some hospitals seem to have high re-admission or postoperative infection rates. Gradually, quality standards for the service are being set and maintained, and failings acted upon. Enterprising fundholders are acting as catalysts for these developments and changes by asking questions locally and discussing quality issues with their local hospitals and the Management Executive of the NHS.

Before assessing the need for any change in contracts between purchasers and providers most fundholders prefer to keep the relationship (often developed over the years) and to encourage service improvements rather than threaten closure or diminution of local services..

As for the rest of the public services, the increasingly high expectation of the patient cannot be ignored, so there is a need for fundholders, acting on behalf of the patient, to ensure the highest quality of service. To this end, fundholder contracts are showing the way forward and the power of exit is beginning to take effect.

Health needs of the population

As a result of the contract data now being collected and analysed by fundholders, a database for the local population is being accurately recorded for the first time. Local incidence and prevalance of disease are becoming statistically valid and, thus, fundholding practices are becoming a source of much information for the assessment of a local population's needs both from a planning of service and a public health point of view.

Future of fundholding

I believe that fundholding will lead the way towards the development of large practices similar to those in the USA. They will become centres of local expertise and, be assisted by local consultants.

Some time away are the specialty hospitals providing high-technology, efficient and short-stay medical services from which patients will return to the community for follow-up by their specialist assisted by their GP.

4

The Preparatory Year

Mercedes Kelly-Madden

The introduction of fundholding gives GPs the opportunity to exercise direct control over NHS resources for the benefit of their patients. It is essential that the preparatory year is planned in advance to prepare for the opportunities that holding a fund gives a practice. The timetable shown below will be subject to regional variation and the responsible officers at the FHSA will advise of the local schedule.

April

As soon as the practice has received official recognition it is advisable to appoint a lead GP, deputy lead GP and a fund manager to form a project team. This should be the core working group who will 'cascade' information to other partners and staff as the preparatory year develops. Collection of practice activity data should begin at this stage. The analysis of this will form the basis of the Region's assessment for the practice fund. As the methodology for data collection varies in every region the responsible FHSA officer will give advice covering which data needs to be collected and how to do this, but a general rule of thumb is to capture information on everything that is referred out of the practice to provider units in this preparatory year. There are now many computerized systems which will help with the data collection exercise. Investigate this with your computer supplier.

May

The practice expenditure programme for the preparatory year will need to be planned now as most FHSAs expect to receive it by the end of June. The earlier it is received at the FHSA the faster the practice has access to the years' management allowance. Again there are regional variations, but the majority of information required is within easy reach in your annual report. The work programme should consist of a maximum of six pages with headings and an outline expenditure of the management allowance. Your FHSA will approve expenditure as soon as the programme has been received and assessed.

Guidance to work expenditure programme

Part 1: the practice population

Detail the catchment area with a brief summary of the population – demography, morbidity and special factors such as ethnicity or deprivation. At this point list any objectives that the practice may wish to achieve within the practice population. Also any tasks and actions required to achieve them, with the likely costs.

Services provided to patients
For this part of the work programme you should find the information readily available in your annual plan. Describe the services offered now, and include any clinics and activities provided. If you have plans to improve or add services which will be related to fundholding include the details here supported by action plans, costs and possible completion dates.

Part 2: the practice staff team

Much of this will be available from the practice report but you will need to expand on any additional staff required to manage the preparatory year, any special skills required and intended salaries. The costs should be included here.

Part 3: the practice premises

This information will be included in your annual report, so a brief description will suffice. If the practice intends to make any improvements, cost and plans should be included.

Part 4: data collection and information systems

This will be unique to the RHA that your practice is situated in and the local FHSA will advise you on how the data should be collected.

Part 5: medical audit activities

Describe any medical audit activities undertaken within the practice and outline your action programme for setting up systems for this and its associated costs.

Part 6: management of the fund

This section should outline the practice's major strengths and the features which will enable it to manage a fund. It should detail those who will have the authority to commission, purchase, approve and negotiate services.

Describe the systems you intend to set up to manage the fund and the associated costs.

Part 7: summary of estimated costs for preparatory work programme

Insert the total costs from each part of your work programme

Part 1	£
Part 2	£
Part 3	£
Part 4	£
Part 5	£
Part 6	£
Part 7 Estimated costs total	£

June

Following approval of the management allowance the practice can appoint a fund manager either from within the practice or from outside it. Regional or FHSA training for GPs and senior staff begins at this time. These courses are usually accredited for the Postgraduate Education Allowance. The following are examples of what is generally available: An introduction to fundholding; Modules on finance and business planning; Contracting and Negotiating skills programmes. The practice should start discussing its business plan and decide who within the practice will be responsible for its collation and production. All the training events around this time will be geared to helping the practice understand the planning process and FHSAs should also complete the business plan on schedule. (If further help is required, see Chapter 18.) The Regional Health Authority will expect to see the finished plan in late September or early October so that GP fundholder business plans can be included in the Regional cyclical planning programme.

July/August

During these months the practice should be monitoring data collection, attending relevant training events and obtaining anticipated practice staffing and prescribing costs from the FHSA for use in the business plan.

September

Submission to the RHA of the business plan. Initial discussions between practices, Health Authorities and provider units commence. At this time the providers should begin to make contact with you in anticipation of 'doing business' with your practice. The senior staff member and project group will need to set aside time for these discussions. The local provider units should be able to give you a directory with their prices and a list of contacts. Seminars for fundholding practices continue.

October/November

The first round of visits by the RHA team begins. This will be the start of your negotiation with the Region over the fund for the practice. The practice will reap the rewards of comprehensive data collection on practice activity at this time. Good data collection will enable you to substantiate figures and aggregated numbers of patients that your Region may have. Remember that this is only the first offer and you will have time to check the figures given and cross-check with those which the practice has kept. The practice should also determine the number of patients on their main provider's waiting lists.

December/January/February

Throughout these months the choice of computer software and hardware should be made. The negotiation of the practice fund will continue during this time. The frenetic pace of the summer will have begun to slow down during these months. The lead GP and fundholding manager will be preparing to set up contracts and negotiating for services with the main providers. The ancillary staff and prescribing costs will be firmed up with the FHSA at this point.

February

Agreement of the proposed fund and confirmation that the practice wishes to proceed to hold a fund from April.

March

The final round of negotiation with main providers and contracts signed.

1 April

Fundholding begins.

Remember that timetables for the preparatory year will vary from Region to Region. Presently, devolvement of responsibility for fundholding to FHSAs is at the top of Regional agendas, and as the FHSAs gear themselves up with resources for fundholders, time-tables will become more evident and the GP fundholding process will begin to slot into Regional and local Health Authority planning cycles.

A sample timetable for preparatory year

April/May	June	July	August	September	October	November	December	January	February	March	April
Training event – Induction Programme for Preparatory Year	Training event – module 2 Principle's of Financial Management- Marketing for Fundholders	Training event – module 3 Business Guidance Planning		Training event – module 4 Negotiating Skills	Training event – module 5 Indicative Prescribing seminar	Training event – module 6 Skills of contracting with Providers	Training event – module 7 Media Training	Final calculation of practice funds. Practice confirms wish to proceed with fundholding	Final negotiation of service agreements	Service agreements signed 'live'	Fund-holding practice
Module 1 Purchasing Health Care					Meeting with FHSA medical adviser for indicative prescribing budgets	In house advertising for those patients who are chronic hospital attenders	Contract discussions with provider units	Installation of software system and training in its use			
Data collection begins in format requested by individual Regions with guidelines issued for collection	Data collection continues	Data collection continues	Data collection continues	Data collection continues	Contact provider units for practice waiting lists	Discussions begin with provider units.	Setting up service agreement	Negotiation continues			
	Work programme devised and agreed with FHSA		Anticipated practice staffing and prescribing costs to be obtained from FHSA for use in business plan.	Business plan for submission to Region and FHSA	Fundholding software and computer selection	Initial visits from Regions and FHSA to discuss fund allocation					

5

The Role of the FHSA

Ian Howarth

The infrastructure of the NHS is continuing to change with these changes being process driven by purchasing consortia/authorities. This may or may not affect accountability. For this chapter I am going to assume that the status quo is to be maintained with FHSAs and DHAs purchasing separately under a joint strategy but retaining a degree of competition from which service improvements and raised standards will ensue.

In order to consider how the role of the FHSA will develop in the management and operation of the general practice funding scheme, it is necessary to outline what their role was in the first wave of 1991/92.

Whilst overall responsibility for implementation of the scheme lay with the RHAs it was decided in some Regions to devolve responsibility wherever possible to the FHSAs. This was the approach adopted in Trent Region of which Lincolnshire is part, and it is from this perspective that I discuss the future of FHSAs in the management of the fundholding scheme.

During the preparatory year the FHSA had to operate against a background of absent regulations, vague and ambiguous guidelines and time constraints. Pressure of time, however was a great propellant and acted as a positive force. It also became clear that local discretion in the absence of regulations and guidelines was required to sustain the momentum of the preparatory activity and to keep the practices 'on the boil'.

In order to maintain consistency within the Region, project managers with joint FHSA/RHA appointments were introduced and made accountable to the FHSA general manager. Meeting on a monthly basis to discuss scheme operation, and offer mutual support they acted as a conduit between the practices and the FHSA. Adopting this approach provided an ideal arrangement which meant that the RHA remained up to date with implementation progress, the FHSA had maximum involvement, gained valuable early experience and the practices enjoyed contact with a local 'friendly' face.

Initial contact

An initial assessment of the practices was conducted to ensure that they were able to satisfy the basic entry criteria and that the practices were adopting an appropriate attitude to the scheme. The Lincolnshire view was that it was better to cultivate future successful practices than maximize the number of scheme entrants. Therefore practices had to be eligible and willing to join without an FHSA 'sales drive' and be able to demonstrate good performance in terms of health targets and GP contract compliance.

It is with a certain degree of ambivalence that Lincolnshire FHSA approaches year two and beyond. Practices have to be monitored in terms of service and financial performance on the one hand and encouraged to develop initiatives and extend services on the other. These two apparently conflicting roles of the FHSA are discussed below, taking the preparation of second wave practices together with the development of first wave practices and then identifying the control and monitoring mechanisms.

Practice management

Any potential fundholder needs to establish sound business management and a robust organizational structure. There are some very good practice managers in post and in some cases it is possible to appoint these people to new management positions. The FHSA should play a major role in helping to make this appointment as they will have been involved in producing job descriptions, placing adverts and attending selection interviews for fundholding managers. New appointees should be on rolling, short-term contracts and performance-related pay should be a feature of their terms of service. Establishing this arrangement paves the way for practice management to be brought into the mainstream NHS management structure – which is an eventuality rather than a possibility.

Some practices have attempted to 'manage' by utilizing some input from an interested partner. Ultimately this is unlikely to work. The relatively steady state of years one and two did not test the manager-partner as they will be in the future when fund management becomes more intense.

The FHSA needs to ensure that all practices preparing for scheme entry have good internal organization and at least comparative equity of funding with other similarly situated practices. The FHSA resource allocation methodologies will vary in their intricacy. It is vital that this resource allocation is completed early to identify what the effect on'the general medical services (GMS) allocation to the practice is before the level of drawings on set-up fees and subsequently management fees can be established. Increases in the GMS allocation are not necessarily for management staff and could include other support staff.

Operationally, the FHSA and practice management structure can work together to institute practice policies, procedures and protocols to provide a firm operational base for the future.

Information technology

FHSAs increasingly have in-house staff to advise practices on systems suppliers, specifications and operations. Using this expertise FHSAs will be guiding practices looking to buy a fundholder system. Each system is modelled on the Department of Health specification with the differences between models being mainly due to user demand for amendments. Practices ought to remember that in buying a system they are buying a company's service too. Therefore it is very important to examine 'helpline' response rates and other aftersales service quality.

In the longer term, FHSAs will be looking towards electronic links with practices. Some of the links currently reported are little more than electronic mailing links. At this stage links might include, monthly financial out-turns and ad-hoc enquiries by the FHSA on the fundholder system into contracts or budget performance. FHSAs are already considering how they might reduce the paper transfer between themselves and fundholders; fax links, floppy disks and modems are currently being investigated.

Business planning

The business plans of the first wave practices were a brave attempt but were largely introspective and philosophical. It was an unreal situation with practices guessing what the potential for savings was, the fund offers being some months away.

Using the first and second wave fund offers as a benchmark, future fundholding practices have produced plans that are more analytical and objective. These plans are valid working documents which map out all future activity.

The FHSA and DHA both have to submit their own business plans to the RHA and are subject to formal review. It seems a logical progression for this arrangement to be carried down to practice level. Progress and development in the future will be driven by structural planning and review. FHSAs would have, at least at this stage, to protect relationships with practices by conducting the reviews without being intrusive.

Fundholders may be wary of such a review process and many would consider it to be an infringement of their right to manage their own resources. However, this argument cannot be sustained because as drawers from the public purse practices are no less accountable than the public authorities for sound financial management.

Contracting

The process of contracting in the first wave was hampered by uncertainty, lack of even semi-accurate costings and the tardiness that existed between units and DHAs. For future waves, the contracting process is not initially dependent on accurate activity data. Even in the early stages practices should have identified what their expectations are of contract content in terms of treatment and patient processing.

The FHSA clearly needs to be involved in the contracting process for several reasons. First, the FHSA can guide the practice on whether the conditions or terms they seek are feasible and ethical. Secondly, the FHSA by being involved can facilitate negotiations and help bring the two parties closer together.

It is essential for health managers to be aware of contracting intentions so that the effects of market forces on patient care and local services can be anticipated. Local priorities and strategies have to be recognized in the contracting process. This is particularly relevant if GPs start to examine the scope for casting a wider net in search of providers.

A natural advance, is the contract which brings consultants in to the surgery and enables consultant services to be bought on a private basis. The benefits here are a local service with GP input and savings on the fund, with a more efficient service provided in terms of access time and cost. The RHA, through the FHSA, will monitor contracts where the practice has established a private company to act as broker.

Ultimately, the contracting process is based on quantified patient flows, treatment and outcomes; and practices should not underestimate the need for accurate, detailed and meaningful data. In addition, the practice should be working with the FHSA to obtain data from their DHA and providers on what is happening locally. There will be disparities and these will need to be investigated. Too much data can be trimmed or discarded, too little will reduce the fund offer, or at the very least leave the practice ill-prepared. In these circumstances practices' contracting confidence will be limited, pushing the fundholder towards block contracts or cost and volume contracts with a high percentage block element.

The term contracting ought to mean that purchasers, fundholders in this case, are adopting a truly commercial manner in securing agreements for their patients' treatments. However, apart from a few isolated instances, producing comparatively small benefits, fundholders have behaved similarly to DHAs in that the existence of a contract was an end in itself.

FHSAs will have a major role to play in the future as commissioning agents. This role evolved in the first wave of contract discussions but dialogue revolved around quality issues like waiting times in out-patient clinics or whether a discharge letter could be faxed within 24 hours. Within this role there will be a need for the FHSA to monitor services in terms of providers' compliance to contracts with fundholders and to identify areas of subsequent or even in-year improvement in performance. Building up a knowledge base will give a clear view to the FHSA of what the non-GP-fundholder should expect to be reflected in local service agreements between the Health Authorities and providers at the round of drafting service agreements. It is recognized that it will be the fundholders who establish new and raised standards with each round of negotiations.

Monitoring arrangements

The control mechanisms on fundholding practices are placed early in the preparatory year and, all working procedures, protocols and computer operations have to reflect standards which will satisfy an audit exercise.

Subsequently, practices in the preparatory year will need to produce an expenditure plan for the set up/management fees and secure agreement from the FHSA to proceed. Practices should bear in mind that the set up fee/management fee is available by agreement and not an automatic entitlement. FHSAs have a responsibility to ensure that value for money is obtained whilst at the same time using local discretion and common sense in pursuit of progress.

Once the practice is operationally tied into the scheme and in addition to the planning review of the practice and personal performance review of the manager, there will be the financial controls which monitor the practice monthly out-turns. FHSAs are preparing themselves to effectively use these documents for routine monitoring and to intervene where appropriate.

Various publications and guidance letters have discussed 'mismanagement' by practices but it is clearly an FHSA's responsibility to anticipate and redress problems. There could be cases where preventive action could not have been taken and the FHSA will then have a damage limitation role. Continuance of the scheme in both cases is for the RHA to decide upon, with advice from the FHSA. The regulations are not comprehensive enough to cover all eventualities ie termination of combined fund operation by one or more practices, on partner death for example, and therefore a contingency policy document which anticipates these circumstances needs to be developed and accepted locally.

Fundholding is a journey, not a destination. FHSAs are acting with the practice as catalyst, facilitator and regulator until the practice is confident enough to make its own way. As mentioned previously the Lincolnshire perspective is to nurture success and build upon it. This can only come from the practice and the FHSA working closely together at every stage.

6

The Fundholding Manager

Lynne Hobden-Clarke

A budget is given to fundholding practices, which they use to buy hospital services, pay practice staff and pay for the drugs they prescribe. The actual management of the fund can be quite daunting to the average practice and a new breed of manager, fundholding managers, has emerged to take this pressure from doctors.

What skills does the new manager need?

The fund manager need not be specially recruited – they may be the existing practice manager or someone already working in the practice. The basic management skills required are those of communication, team building, organizational and training ability linked with financial awareness, computer literacy, statistics and an understanding of negotiating contracts. Some practice managers will relish the opportunity of a challenge and will be willing to attend training to enhance their financial planning and monitoring skills. Some will plead, quite rightly, that practice management is already a full-time role and there is no room for another major responsibility. For these reasons many practices choose to recruit a person from the business world. There is no doubt that a business background will provide many of the additional skills required to run a fund, however, these can also be present in a well-motivated practice manager.

There is no right or wrong choice, it will depend entirely upon the views and resources of each individual practice.

The implications of using an existing manager

The whole practice staffing and reporting procedures will need to be reviewed to allow for the dual role. Routine duties will need to be delegated to a deputy to create time for managing the fund and secretarial time may also be needed to remove some of the burden of administration and deal with correspondence. A data entry clerk is essential to feed patient activity information into the fundholding software. To pay a manager to do this would be a shameful waste of resources. Although fundholding is quite separate in administrative terms, the ability to take an overview and translate fundholding decisions into implications for the practice is a definite advantage.

The implications of recruiting a manager

The alternative to using an existing manager is to recruit a manager for fundholding. How do you find such a person, and what constitutes 'relevant experience'? Initially, there was a lot of publicity about needing someone with an accounting background. Lately this has shifted in emphasis to 'entrepreneurial' skills. This suggests that to have held a senior post in a profit-making organization would be suitable.

The greatest dangers lie in the selection procedure. It is imperative that the partners have a clear idea of the role they expect, and to be agreed upon it. To formulate a job description crystallizes thoughts and will bring differing perceptions to light. There may be conflict in the roles of the practice manager and the fund manager, and the job descriptions of both can be dovetailed before the new person arrives. The existing practice manager must be involved in formulating the job descriptions, and be quite clear about the partners reasons for splitting the management responsibilities. The job titles should convey the function, for example 'business manager', 'fund manager' or 'operations manager'. Avoid using ambiguous terms, for example 'executive manager'.

Practice implications

Staff

The implications on the practice staff need to be evaluated, and some reassurance may be necessary. Try producing a chart showing each person's position and the reporting procedure. The staff will need to be informed about the new structure and the possibility of additional staff for fundholding. It is a good idea to invite staff to apply for the new posts, again reducing the general resistance to such a major change. *See* Figures 6.1 and 6.2.

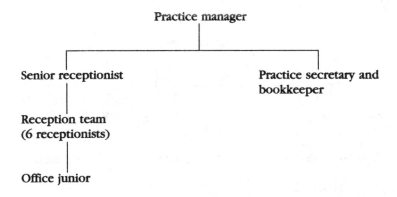

Figure 6.1: Staffing structure before fundholding.

No matter how the fund is going to be managed there is an inevitable increase in staff, either recruited specifically for fundholding or by restructuring the practice to release time for fundholding, or both. The impact on the practice expenses needs to be costed, although some of the additional staff can be paid from the management fee. This has the advantage of being a 100% reimbursed instead of the usual 70%.

Space

Where will all these people work, and is there enough space for the additional computers to run the software? Most

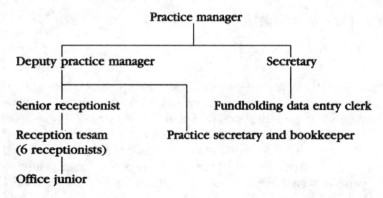

Figure 6.2a: Using the existing practice manager to manage the fundholding practice.

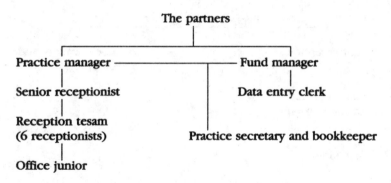

Figure 6.2b: Recruiting a fund manager.

premises are already in dire need of administrative space and this may precipate some necessary extensions or alterations. Again, help may be at hand from the FHSA in the shape of an improvement grant.

Communication

Fundholding has a general impact on the overall standards of communication within the practice. The doctors must pass the details of each referral, investigation and X-ray ordered to the fund manager or data entry clerk. As time progresses and freedom to place contracts increases the partners must also have some agreement about the consultants to whom they refer, and why. In most practices referral options have been quite personal and not even discussed with colleagues. Suddenly not only the doctors' views, but those of patients, need to be included in the equation. Patient questionnaires about the service that they have received, either as an out-patient or an in-patient, are part of the evaluation process. Not only should they include questions like 'did the consultant explain clearly what was wrong?', but 'was the waiting area clean and pleasant?', and 'did you feel there were enough nurses available?'. The fund manager must collate all these comments and be able to present them to the partners when the time for placing contracts comes around.

Time must be set aside for regular partnership meetings to be devoted exclusively to managing the fund and the contracts. Also for staff training to keep them up to date with practice policies and preferences. In addition, there are many meetings with other agencies, for example the FHSA, RHA, local hospital managers and consultants, all of which will take time away from the patients. The fund manager should have the correct skills to be able to participate in all of these meetings and possibly attend them alone if a partner is unavailable.

Therefore the fund manager must be a good communicator and have the ability to facilitate these types of discussions.

Salaries

So what should this 'supermanager' be paid? The Whitley Council scale descriptions suggest Grade 8 'a practice manager with a range of complex duties requiring investigations, recommendations and actions'; or Grade 9 'a practice manager with a range of complex duties and responsibility for introducing new systems and making policy input'. This places the range of salary between £20,575 and £27,077 per annum. To attract an experienced manager from the business world, or to stop your own practice manger leaving for another fundholding practice these salaries are essential!

Conclusion

The fund manager cannot work in isolation. Many fundholding decisions have an impact on the general running and organization of the practice, and practice policies have an impact on fundholding. It does not matter if the management is one role or subdivided into two, communication must be strong. It will help considerably if a partner takes on the executive responsibility for fundholding. Not only is some clinical input invaluable, but also for the balance and rationalization of views of partners, managers and staff.

In conclusion, the skills required of a fundholding manager are exactly the same as a competent practice manager.

7

Business Planning in General Practice

Antoinette Pirie

There are three fundamental components of the management task which apply in any organization:

- policy decisions
- strategy decisions
- operational decisions.

Policy decisions

Addressing practice policy requires an insight into the forces that motivate practice members and the values and principles that make them want to be in the 'business' of primary health care delivery.

In general practice the policy issues tend to get built-in and are assumed to be self-evident. Taking time to turn implicit assumptions into explicit ideas can go a long way towards deriving a focus for the practice. No group can act effectively without a clear direction and it is the partner's responsibility to involve all members of the practice team at this level in the decision-making process.

Strategy decisions

Strategy is concerned with the broad brush strokes of how to put these visions into effect. Strategic considerations should address the following issues:

- The scope of a practice's activities – does (and should) the practice concentrate on one area of activity, or does it have many? Should it contemplate a wider role in the provision of health services, for example, alternative medicine? This analysis is essential as it concerns the way in which those responsible for managing the practice view its boundaries.

- Matching the activities of the practice to the environment in which it operates.

- Matching the practice activities to its resource capability – strategy is not just about countering environmental threats and taking advantage of environmental opportunities, it is also about matching organizational resources to these threats and opportunities. There would be little point in trying to take advantage of some new opportunity if the resources needed were not available, could not be made available or it if the strategy was rooted in an inadequate resource base.

- The values and expectations of those who have power in the practice. In some respects strategy can be regarded as the reflection of the attitudes and beliefs of those with the most influence in the organization.

- The direction in which the practice is moving in the long term.

- The implications for change throughout the practice.

Operational decisions

In the next phase the broad strategic plans are elaborated into specific programmes for every day operational tasks, to 'keep the show on the road'.

Business planning

The business plan can be regarded as a means of expressing the practice policy, strategy and operational decisions in a form which can be used by management. A clear and systematic approach to business planning is central to the successful running of any business.

Aims of a business plan

- To set:
    - goals
    - targets
    - milestones.
- To measure achievement against a plan.
- To structure and record the planning process
    - identification of options
    - evaluation of options.
- To demonstrate commitment and agreement.
- To provide a business management tool for:
    - control
    - feedback
    - delegation
    - accountability.

Preparing a business plan will provide an insight into the planning process. It is actually this process which is important to the long term health of any organization and not simply the plan that emerges from it. Practices are dynamic, as are the environments in which they operate. No one expects every event recorded in the plan to occur as predicted but the understanding and knowledge created by the process of business planning will prepare the practice for any changes it may face and so enable it to adjust swiftly.

A business plan should be regarded as a key management tool, it should attempt to answer these questions:

- Where do you want the practice to be in five years time?
- How are you going to achieve it?
- Will the proposed plan work?

There are a number of alternative approaches to business planning but most are essentially composed of the same stages:

- definition of objectives and a statement of values
- evaluation of current position and internal assessment
- review of external environment
- preparation of practice strategy
- financial forecasts
- preparation of an action plan.

Figure 7.1: The planning hierarchy.

Definition of objectives and statement of values

The practice needs a clear identity, an agreement on mission and a statement of aims. This will involve an assessment of the past and intentions for the future. It can be regarded as a reappraisal and reaffirmation of goals. What is hoped to be achieved in the short and long-term for the practice as a whole, for the individual practice members and for the patients served? *See* Figure 7.2.

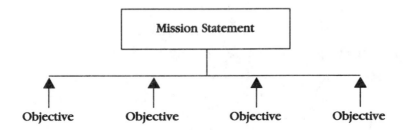

- Official goals
- unofficial goals
- measurable objectives.

Figure 7.2: Definition of objectives.

These concepts can be encapsulated in a mission statement. The mission should be narrow enough to give direction and guidance to everyone in the practice, but wide enough to allow growth and realization of potential. Above all mission statements should be realistic, achievable and brief.

> **'A mission statement should identify what you want your practice to be doing. This may differ from what it is doing now.'** A well-defined mission statement that challenges your practice will provide the focus for the rest of the business planning process.

Evaluation of current position and internal assessment

This analysis should concentrate on strengths and weaknesses within the practice. What is done well and what is done badly? Are there any obvious reasons why?

Frankness and honesty can be difficult, as can keeping to a timetable during the whole planning process, so an outside facilitator can be invaluable at this stage. An independent assessor is also far more likely to be impartial and less prone to let personalities interfere. Some aspects of the practice that should be covered at this stage include:

- list details
- clinical and non-clinical services offered
- patients' perception of service
- staff profile - job descriptions
            - staff skills
- practice management - organization structure
                      - lines of reporting
                      - management expertise
                      - skill deficits
- practice premises
- computer activities and support
- activity levels - surgery hours
                  - specialty clinics
                  - targets
- referral data
- prescribing data
- financial management.

Looking at these and other issues, depending on individual practices, it will be possible to derive a practice profile which highlights particular strengths and elucidates any weaknesses.

Carry out an external assessment

The overall aim in this part of the evaluation is to identify opportunities for the practice and target any potential threats. Areas that should be addressed include:

- list trends, both short and long-term
- local growth/contraction factors - housing developments, business relocation
- demographic trends in relation to the practice - location of retirement homes in the area, for example

- a broad view of the competition – conventional and alternative. A practice does not operate in isolation and a business plan cannot be compiled without reference to other practices and agencies. Are they in competition or would collaboration be a good idea?

- the relationship with the FHSA, Health Authority and RHA needs to be examined and developed if necessary.

Grouped together the above analyses are often referred to as a SWOT analysis (strengths, weaknesses, opportunities, threats).

Preparation of a practice strategy

Once the practice's overall position is known it is possible to begin drawing up specific strategies to maximize progress. The aim should be to build on the strengths and eradicate the weaknesses that have been determined during the preceding analysis.

During this stage of the planning process attention should be turned to the issues that the practice has to get right to be successful and, in this new environment, to survive. These are referred to as Critical Success Factors and can range from computer capacity to links with a provider unit.

Look at where you want the practice to be in three or five years time. Objectives reflect not only what you want the practice to achieve but also what you think it can achieve. Some will fall out of the practice analysis that you have produced. For most practices, the objectives will be concerned with patient service, financial performance and with future plans for staff and premises.

Objectives must be:

- quantifiable
- within a defined time scale, and
- realistic and achievable.

If your objectives fulfil these three criteria, they will serve as useful goals and yardsticks against which to judge your performance. They will help you monitor the progress and the achievements of your practice.

Financial forecasts

Practices will need to prepare the following financial statements for two years:

- profit and loss account
- cash flow forecast
- balance sheet.

Year 1: monthly profit and loss and cash flow projections.
Year 2: quarterly profit and loss and cash flow projections.

Balance sheets should be produced at the end of each financial year.

The use of computerized spreadsheets in developing financial projections can make the whole process much simpler, particularly when performing a 'what if' analysis.

Preparation of a detailed action plan

Aims and strategies have to be turned into systems for running the practice and to ensure the improvement of health care for patients. Business plans do not implement themselves, therefore, a detailed plan of action needs to be drawn up to ensure that the planned outcome actually occurs. It will need to address:

- the tasks that need to be performed
- individual responsibilities for the tasks
- timescales involved
- quality measurements.

Many potential fundholders will have been asked to prepare a practice business plan by the RHA as part of their application to join the fundholding scheme. For many it will have involved a lot of extra work in an already tight schedule with little under-

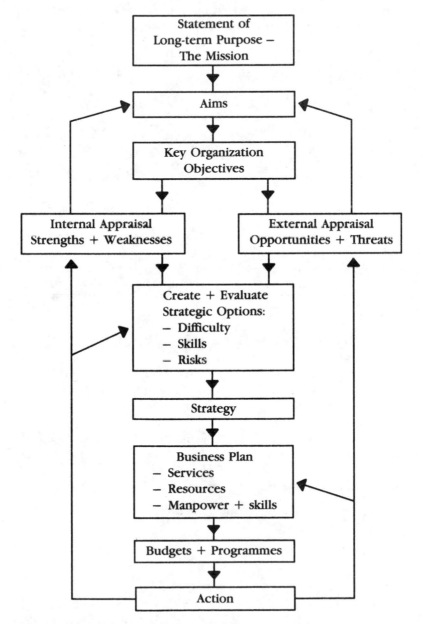

Figure 7.3: Business planning process.

standing of its relevance. Once drawn up, however, a business plan can be used on a working basis as a framework with which to manage all aspects of the practice. *See* Figure 7.3.

8

Contracting for General Practice Fundholders

Antoinette Pirie

NHS contracts are the means through which purchasers and providers of health care will agree on the required quality, quantity and cost of the services to be provided for their population. Using contracts as a focus for raising standards is perhaps the key objective behind their introduction.

The contracting environment

The proposals for contractual funding of hospital and community health services are designed to promote efficiency and enhance consumer choice.

- **The benefit for purchasers** (GP fundholders and Health Authorities) is that they can seek to meet the health care needs of their resident populations in a way which makes the most cost-beneficial use of their resources.

- **The benefit for providers** is that services can be planned to operate at the most efficient level by attracting funding from a number of different purchasers in direct relation to the level of activity.

The purchasing role enables Health Authorities and fundholders to specify much more precisely than in the past exactly what services they aim to secure for their populations and the way those services are provided. Commissioning agencies will need to ensure that their priorities and the service agreements they enter into truly reflect the health needs of their given population. Furthermore, the providers of health care will be challenged to provide services at a given level of quality and cost.

Moving to contractual funding has lead to new responsibilities and relationships for those involved. This section briefly outlines the basics of the different roles of the agencies involved.

The role of the Regional Health Authority

- To provide a strategic framework within which contracts agreed reflect the RHA's priorities in terms of overall equitable distribution of resources.

- To facilitate the contracting environment by ensuring a smooth process of reaching contracts and service agreements.

- To provide a conciliation service.

- To maintain a dialogue with purchasers, in particular GP fundholders.

- To review/monitor plans for the use of funds in relation to overall DHA assessment of need.

The role of the Health Authorities

DHAs and commissioning agencies have moved away from planning services and managing their delivery towards identifying the service requirements of a resident population and planning and managing their purchase.

Their tasks include:

- securing contracts which best reflect the health needs of the population for which they are responsible

- ensuring that their population has good access to a comprehensive range of high quality, value for money, hospital and community health services

- satisfying themselves that they are placing contracts in line with GP's referral preferences, and have in place arrangements to handle any extra-contractual referrals.

The main process for meeting these responsibilities is the specification of services required and negotiation of appropriate contracts.

The role of the Family Health Services Authority

- To determine priorities for meeting health care needs along-side the commissioning agencies.

- To develop a brokerage role by representing GP fundholders and non-fundholders in discussions about developing contracts with commissioning agencies and provider units.

- To work with commissioning agencies to ensure that contracting decisions satisfy GP referral patterns.

- To monitor non-fundholding GP referrals against contracts and GP expenditure against indicative allocations.

- To determine the limitations on non-fundholding GPs making extra-contractual referrals in consultation with commissioning agencies and the Local Medical Committee (LMC).

The role of fundholding GPs

Part of the DHA's responsibilities for securing services have been taken over by practices which hold practice funds.
   The fundholding practices need:

- to identify the health needs of their practice population

- to negotiate, place and monitor contracts with appropriate providers

- to maintain a dialogue with the RHA via the FHSA

- to produce annual fundholding accounts for the FHSA.

The role of non-fundholding GPs

- To link in with the work of the commissioning agency on the identification of health needs.

- To identify health needs within their practice population.

- To link in with the commissioning agency network for the agreement and monitoring of contracts.

The role of the provider unit

In the past provider units could expect an assured level of funding from one major source but had to restrict their activity level to match this. Now their level of activity is chiefly constrained by their ability to attract contract funding from purchasers. Providers now need to keep in close touch with the plans of their major purchasers and so be able to anticipate the services they will require in the future. Many also want to widen their range of 'customers'. Provider units will wish to ensure that referring GPs are happy with the services provided, in view of the central role which GPs play in determining the pattern of referrals.

Managers of health care units have moved away from delivering services within the policies and budget of a particular authority towards delivering contracted services within quantity and quality specifications to a number of clients in return for agreed levels of income. In effect their task is:

- to attract contracts from purchasers in order to ensure their viability

- to provide services at agreed levels of quality and cost. GP fundholders will be contracting with:

- directly managed units (DMUs)

- NHS trusts

- the private sector.

Units have drawn up descriptions of their services (a prospectus) to help ensure that potential purchasers are aware of what is on offer and can compare this with offers from other purchasers.

The contracting process

The roles and relationships outlined above enable the development of a contracting process – namely service specification, supply proposal, negotiation and review. The approach to con-

tracts arises out of the roles and responsibilities of the purchasers and the suppliers, and concentrates on service specification and standards of service as two essential components of
the contractual process.

The steps of the contracting process for GP fundholders.

1. Identification of treatment patterns for services covered by
   the fund, including levels of activity and location.
2. Discussion of proposed referral patterns with the RHA/
   FHSA.
3. Discussions with provider units about possible terms of
   contracts, eg prices.
4. Discussion with the RHA/Agency about the level of funding
   necessary to lay contracts for hospital services.
5. Entering into provisional contracts with provider units.
6. Final commitment to contract after decision to run a fund.

Purchasers are responsible for specifying their requirements
for a given period of time: in the case of fundholders, one year.
This analysis will be based on priorities, local epidemiological
forecasts and historical referral data. A practice needs assessment and anticipated changes in requirements can be regarded
as the first essential step towards drawing up a service agreement. Fundholding practices need to set out their requirements
for each of the services for which they are going to contract.
The purchaser's requirement statements are free-standing
documents to be offered to suppliers for them to respond to
with supply proposals. A number of Regions have helped to
formalize this process by issuing guideline 'service requirements'.
   GPs will need to ask themselves:

• Are we happy with the current service?

• Which areas need changing and which do not?

• What are our priorities for change?

• What are realistic targets to aim for (both short-term and
  long-term)?

Choosing between suppliers

The service requirements can be offered to more than one supplier with the supply proposals being used as the basis for choice. It is, however, not suggested that anything approaching a full-blown competitive tendering exercise is entered into. There will be circumstances where there is only one possible supplier. In other cases the purchaser's knowledge of potential suppliers may mean that, subject to satisfactory supply proposals, they may be content to use their existing supplier and do not need to invite competing proposals.

Where a choice between suppliers needs to be made that judgment should not be on comparative cost alone, but rather on efficiency and quality as well.

Arriving at contracts: negotiation and agreement

Contracts are in effect, if not literally, an amalgamation of the service requirement and the relevant supply proposal, modified as required by discussion and negotiation between the purchaser and the supplier.

Content of the contract

The contractual process should cover all aspects of the services to be provided and the expectation of both parties. A fundamental merit of contractual funding is the stimulation it gives to a much better articulation of what health service providers are expected to achieve. A service agreement or contract as a minimum should specify:

- the nature and amount of services to be provided (the approach adopted will depend to an extent on the type of contract in question)
- duration of the contract
- general or specific population characteristics (particularly relevant to block contracts)

- volumes and prices
- facilities that will be employed
- staffing requirements
- confidentiality
- the criteria for admission and discharge of in-patients and for day/out-patient referrals (a different approach needed depending on the contract type)
- the speed with which patients will get access to services and the approach to prioritization
- other quality measures to be applied
- responsibility for tertiary referrals
- subcontracting
- responsibility for clinical complications
- information the parties will make available to each other (this will include, where appropriate, nationally agreed minimum data sets)
- means of monitoring the contract, including access to premises and data
- payment schedules
- mechanics of billing, authorization and settlement.

Attached to the broad service agreements will be more detailed individual service specifications which have been agreed between the purchaser and the provider.

Initially the service agreements were largely statements of present activity, not least because of time and data limitations. It is important however that service specifications contribute to the way in which contracts can offer a focus for raising standards and describe what, resources permitting, services should be. The way in which these can come together, and be related to what services will cost and the resources available, is an essential part of the process by which the initial service specification is translated, in negotiation with suppliers, into the actual agreement.

Choice of contract type

There are three main contract types in operation:

- block
- cost and volume
- cost per case/limited volume

with possible hybrids of the three. *See* Figure 8.1.

The decision on which type to use depends on a range of factors, including:

- availability of information on which to base negotiations
- objectives and incentives inherent in different types of contract
- the volume of services to be purchased
- cost of contracting, including negotiation and monitoring costs
- the presence or lack of competition.

Block contracts

The block contract covers access to a defined range of services at the provider unit in return for an annual fee payable in monthly instalments. The provider will need information on the approximate level of demand from the purchaser.

In using block contracts there is the risk of paying for services which prove to be unnecessary and which could lock up a significant proportion of a relatively small budget. The number of patients which individual fundholders will be referring will be small when compared with the DHA/Health Agency and block contracts will not cater for the variations in need which will occur amongst a smaller pool of patients. Block contracts may, however, be suitable for practices purchasing as a consortium or where the data on treatment rates is not yet well established.

A developmental approach has been essential. The contracts

	Block	Cost and volume	Cost per case
Specification	Defined population	Volume level	Individual cases
Limit	Open ended	Specified volume priorities	Provider capacity OR purchaser
Effect of under-utilization	Provider surplus/ Purchaser wastage	Provider surplus/ Purchaser wastage	Purchaser could redeploy funds
Implementation forward	Easy to roll	Need to set level	Detailed costing
Monitoring information	Patient residence only	Patient residence and type of procedure	Diagnosis and/or procedure in detail
Monitoring costs	Low	Medium	High
Checks against volume	None except resistence	Tally numbers against list	Tally numbers against maxima
Flexibility	Low	Medium	High
Price relative to cost	High	Medium	Low (marginal), given fixed costs covered

Figure 8.1: Choice of contract type.

first let were relatively crude and have been refined at each contract review. While the direction for refinement does need to be clear, it is of value that improvements follow from actual experience. An approach that attempted to reach an 'ideal' position at one step would have been more likely to result in contracts which were either over-complicated or much too relaxed.

With experience all contracts will become more specific. Eventually block contracts may be as well defined as cost and volume and cost per case. However, the continuing distinction will be that, although they will be negotiated in the context of forecasts about the likely volume of patients to be treated, block contracts are essentially about purchasing access to facilities, rather than a defined baseline of cases or treatments. They will therefore have the advantage that they allow providers more flexibility in coping with demand, but the disadvantage that they define less precisely what is being purchased for the price. It is also likely that some services will always need to be provided under block contracts.

Advantages

- Closest to pre-91 practice.

- Least demanding on activity information.

- Maximum flexibility for the provider.

Disadvantages

- Getting the incentives right – providers obligations are limited – purchaser may pay for unused capacity.

- Demand may be unpredictable and therefore present difficulties for the provider.

- Difficulties in making service and quality requirements explicit.

These problems may make it necessary to develop costly monitoring mechanisms to secure quality and efficiency particularly where competition is limited. There are cases for developing a hybrid form of block contract ie building in a workload agreement. These developments begin to relate activity to payment and incentives can be built in.

Cost and volume contracts

Cost and volume contracts specify the number of treatments or procedures to be provided for a specific price. The fixed element is also payable in monthly instalments.

Cost and volume contracts are more useful to fundholders. They have data collected through the practice records which will provide figures for the incidence of particular disorders and procedures and enable them to specify what they require for a fixed fee. Cost and volume contracts can also provide the flexibility to meet variations in need for services, since they can be arranged for a set level of procedures with the possibility of exceeding that number if necessary. Cost and volume contracts have the capacity to cover a range of procedures for which an average price has been set. This type of contract can be used, for example, for the majority of surgical procedures covered by the fund.

Advantages

- Links payment with activity and maintains financial control – incentives right for the purchaser.

- Financial security for the provider but greater flexibility than with the other two types of contract.

Disadvantages

- Detailed information requirements for costing, monitoring and invoicing related to the costs of specificity.

- Purchaser wastes resources if money is committed to a fixed volume of treatments and these are not fully used.

- Costs of negotiation.

Cost per case and limited volume contracts

Arranged on a price per case/limited volume basis. These contracts should probably be reserved for 'one-off' or small volume contracts, perhaps in circumstances where the costs of treatment warrant separate pricing. These contracts are likely to be used more by fundholders than DHAs, because of the smaller scale of their contracting exercise.

Apart from their particular value for purchasing treatments which are less common in the smaller populations dealt with by fundholders, they can give fundholders the ability to purchase treatments more cheaply or more quickly using the marginal costing and capacity principles – fundholders might be able to negotiate with the provider units to supply treatment for individual patients using any unanticipated spare capacity which the units might have in a year. There is a risk of the service not being available. If fundholders are looking to 'spot buy' they need to ascertain from the provider the likely scope for in-year 'spot buying' and probably reserve it for a limited range of procedures.

Disadvantages

- high transaction costs
- detailed information costs.

Most suitable for

- rare one-off cases
- part of a variable volume agreement added on to a cost and volume contract
- 'spot buys'.

Contract options

Fundholders will have to contract for:

- certain in-patient and day-case procedures (*see* Appendix 1)
- all out-patient attendances except antenatal, neonatal and genitourinary clinics
- direct access for: physiotherapy, speech therapy and occupational therapy, chiropody and dietetics
- direct access for pathology services and X-rays
- domiciliary consultations
- health visiting and community nursing, elements of learning disabilities and mental health services.

The contracts fundholders will place can relate to each area separately or various combinations.

All initial out-patient referrals are covered by the scheme and fundholders will be able to choose whether to lay contracts for out-patient diagnosis and advice alone, or for diagnosis and appropriate treatment arising from the initial referral. To an extent the type of contract will depend on the way in which prices for out-patient referrals are quoted.

With medical conditions, where GPs are more likely to be referring for diagnosis and advice on condition management, a contract which covers all initial out-patient appointments for a particular speciality is appropriate.

Surgical procedures, general and otherwise, on the list of in-patient treatments covered by the fund are amongst those commonly seen by larger practices. Fundholders should be in a good position to predict the likely outcome of the out-patient referral for many of these cases. Some of the surgical procedures may lend themselves to an 'all-in' contract which specifies out-patient appointment, in-patient treatment and follow-up care.

It is recommended that contracts include procedures for informing GPs if the treatment differs from that specified in the contract although it is assumed that fundholders will normally wish to refer patients on the basis that the provider will carry out whatever treatment is needed without further authorization from the practice.

The price for a referral will contain an allowance for an average number of non-attenders.

Duration

It is advantageous for both providers and fundholders if as many contracts as possible are arranged in advance. Fundholders will be assured that they have the ability to treat their patients and provider units will have the security of knowing that a certain level of funding will be available to them from this source.

The duration of the contracts will vary according to the type; it will be most critical with block contracts. Providers will need reasonable security before deploying the necessary resources – purchasers will want to ensure continuity of care. Fundholders' contracts operate on an annual basis.

Quality

The contractual process should be regarded as a means of improving the quality of services provided. Purchasers will want to examine both clinical and non-clinical aspects in specifying and letting contracts. In particular they will want to be reassured that the contract will seek to guarantee:

- the appropriateness of treatment and care
- an optimum clinical outcome
- a minimum chance of complications and similar preventable events
- an appropriate environment
- convenience for patients/relatives/friends
- patient involvement, if wished.

For many aspects of care, indicators will need to be used as quality monitoring devices.

Consumer satisfaction

Because of the White Paper's emphasis on the patient as consumer, consumer satisfaction is a good starting point. A fundholder might ask to see the following.

1. The information given to patients about the organization of the hospital and what they can expect to happen to them during their stay. What information are they given about their condition and treatment?
2. Patient satisfaction survey data.
3. Details of how complaints are handled.
4. Data on waiting lists and waiting times.

Clinical care

These can either be:

- general measures of clinical care (readmission rates, infection rates etc), or
- indicators relevant to particular conditions or treatments.

Either sort of indicator can deal with structure, process or outcome. For example, taking some general indicators:

Structure indicators

- staffing data – ratio of qualified to unqualified staff
- number of training schemes with full accreditation.

Process indicators

- percentage of first out-patient visits where a patient is seen by a consultant
- waiting times to out-patient appointment and to treatment
- percentage of day.case work undertaken by specialty.

Outcome indicators

- infection rates
- readmission rates by specialty
- complication rates, anaesthetic reactions, adverse drug reactions
- length of stay as a proxy measure for complication rates
- death as a percentage of discharges.

This is getting to be very complex information to monitor. The purchaser would need to know what sort of answers are acceptable. For some indicators, for example length of stay, there are national averages by specialty but for others information would need to be collected to give comparisons or the purchasers would need to make their own judgment about acceptability. The fundholder may be better off saying, 'we expect you to have good infection control procedures and your own mechanism for monitoring infection rates', rather than asking for detailed statistics.

In future it is likely that clinical indicator development will be less concerned with these general measures than with specific diseases and conditions. What consumers, and therefore a purchaser acting on their behalf, wants to know is the relative risk associated with a particular procedure and the outcome statistics of the facility where the procedure is to be performed.

Contracts also open the door to specifying the appropriateness of the treatment for a particular set of clinical indications. An initial step in this direction would be for purchasers to decide at what point in the spread of a new technique or procedure they are willing to purchase it for their population.

Organizational standards

There are many activities which go on in a hospital which help in the overall aim of ensuring high-quality patient care. These will also need to be addressed, for example:

- health and safety regulations and good practice – how far does the hospital comply? For example, when did the environmental health officer last inspect the kitchens?

- how are the internal and external cleaning contractors monitored?

- is there evidence that the hospital has an effective infection control policy?

- are drug formularies in use?

- what quality assurance methods are in operation? Is medical audit established across all specialties and working satisfactorily?

Some of the main issues to be addressed in defining quality for inclusion in contracts are:

- whether the purchaser or the provider will drive the process

- the fact that different customers/clients may have different preferences
- the level of detail to be specified in contracts
- the monitoring mechanisms to be established
- the cost of improving and monitoring quality.

As mentioned above, related to this are the different approaches to the relationship between the purchaser and the provider in quality specification. These can include:

- full specification for every service and detailed monitoring arrangements
- a requirement that systems eg medical audit are in place in the provider units
- exception reporting
- mutual trust.

Most quality measures will fall into five broad categories:

- guarantees of adhering to legal requirements. National codes of practice or explicit standards
- the provision of systems, such as medical audit, intended to assure quality
- setting of specific standards or key indicators of performance on matters of general concern or specific local interest
- setting specific clinical outcome requirements both applicable and related to specific clinical conditions
- 'common law' – a general assumption of standards which could reasonably be expected from a hospital operating in a UK medical environment.

Quality measures should only be introduced into contracts if they:

- are significant
- can be readily measured

- improvements can be made
- have relevance to the patient
- do not trigger excessive expectations, and
- are under the providers' control.

Access to premises and data

Contracts should provide for purchasers to be able to pay both announced and unannounced visits to the health care units specified in contracts to check whether standards as promised in the specification are being provided. The purchaser should also have access to any data which is specified in the contract as being necessary to its monitoring.

Pricing

Suppliers have worked out the prices they propose to charge for their services and this will form a major part of their supply proposals.

Pricing for fundholders' contracts follow three basic principles:

- prices should be based on costs
- costs should generally be full costs
- there should be no planned cross-subsidization.

The stated price or prices within a contract will obviously reflect the type of contract and quantity involved. If a contract is for a particular speciality it may be necessary to negotiate prices which reflect different types of workload within that speciality. The factors the provider will assess in deriving a price include:

- quantity (number and severity)
- quality
- costs (fixed and variable)
- competitive price level.

In setting prices the provider will give consideration to both current costs and to prospective increases during the contract period. Some DHA contracts may include clauses for price variation in response to unpredicted events. This is considered to be inappropriate for fund-holder's contracts because:

- they will have much less scope than DHAs to hold sums in reserve for such eventualities

- fundholders' contracts will have the maximum duration of one year so there will be much less uncertainty for provider units.

Prices of fundholders' contracts will therefore be fixed.
The issues the purchaser will need to address include:

- is the price affordable?

- is it a fair price for the service in question?

- is there scope for the supplier to improve on the price offered?

- what modification of the service specification would bring the price to an affordable level?

In addressing these questions the first aim of the fundholder, where prices were not affordable or seemed not to be fair, would be to secure a change in price. They would be helped in this if they had 'benchmarks' of costs for different types of treatment.

Disputes

The aim of the new contractual basis for health care is to maximize the health care provision resulting from spending tax-payers' money. Contracting should maximize the total quantity and quality of service and no District, doctor or hospital will be allowed to exploit short-term competitive advantages. Purchaser or provider cartels, or abuse of a monopoly position will not be permitted.

The legal aspects of fundholding are addressed fully in Chapter 9.

Monitoring

Both the purchaser and provider need to agree a monitoring mechanism which will identify any variations from the agreed contract. This mechanism will benefit from a small number of key indicators which reveal that the contract is on course.

Conclusion

Contracts, together with the separation of the purchaser/provider functions and the emphasis on devolution, provide an important vehicle through which the patient has priority and quality and efficiency improvements are a primary goal.

There are some important points to be remembered in the new environment:

- establishing an NHS contract should be not be approached as a legalistic or adversarial exercise but as an opportunity to discuss and agree how improvements to patient care can be secured

- medical, nursing and other professional staff should be involved in looking at existing service strengths and weaknesses, and agreeing service specifications and standards for inclusion in contracts

- the needs and views of patients should increasingly influence the delivery of the service at all levels

- the contracting process should be viewed as developmental and the degree and speed of change can only be determined locally.

9

The Legal Aspects of Fundholding

Tim Young

This chapter deals with the requirements for recognition as a fundholding practice and some of the legal issues to be addressed in connection with fundholding status. The law is stated as at 1 April 1993.

Eligibility

Any one or more medical practitioners providing general medical services in accordance with arrangements under Section 29 of the National Health Services Act 1977 (the '1977 Act') may apply to the relevant Regional Health Authority for recognition as a fundholding practice – Section 14(1) National Health Service and Community Care Act 1990 (the '1990 Act'). A medical practitioner who becomes a fundholder remains a general practitioner within the NHS. The National Health Service (General Medical Services) Regulations 1992 continue to apply to him.

The relevant RHA for these purposes is the one in whose Region lies the whole or the greater part of the practice's Family Health Services Authority's locality. The relevant FHSA is the one on whose medical list the members of the practice are included. Where the medical practitioners wishing to make the application are on different FHSAs' lists, then the relevant FHSA is determined as if they were all practising in a single partnership and will be the one in whose locality resides the largest number of patients on the practice list.

In the case of Scotland, application is made to the relevant Health Board and in Wales to the Secretary of State.

It is not necessary for the medical practitioners making an

application to be in partnership. Practices can group together for this purpose and smaller practices may need to do so to meet the eligibility requirements.

The National Health Service (Fund-holding Practices) Regulations 1993 ('the 1993 Regulations') deal with the recognition and operation of fundholding practices in England and Wales. There are equivalent Regulations for Scotland.

Conditions for recognition

The relevant RHA cannot grant recognition, in cases of practices grouping together, where the prospective fundholding practice includes both a member who practises in partnership and the total number of patients on the lists of patients of that partnership exceeds 7,000, and a member who practises in another such partnership. The intention is presumably to avoid the creation of excessively large individual fundholding practices. This does not prevent practices getting together in consortia. Subject to the above qualification the RHA is required to grant recognition where it is satisfied that all of the following conditions are fulfilled.

1. On the date of application there is a total of at least 7,000 patients on the lists of patients of members of the practice, or in the opinion of the RHA it is likely that there will be a total of at least 7,000 patients on those lists on the date on which any recognition would take effect.

2. Where some or all of the members of the practice are practising in partnership, the application is made (whether or not with some other persons, eg on a grouping of practices) by all the members of the partnership. Individual members of the partnership will not therefore be able to opt out of joining the scheme and still remain partners.

3. The practice is in the opinion of the RHA capable of managing an allotted sum effectively and efficiently and, in particular, it possesses, or has access to, equipment, such as computers, and expertise necessary to enable it to do so. The phrase 'effectively and efficiently' introduces value for

money concepts. Is the allotted sum being used to meet the objectives for which it is provided and in a cost-effective manner?

4. The members of the practice agree to comply with the conditions for continuing recognition (*see* below).

5. Where the members of the practice are not partners in a single partnership, the members of the practice have entered into an agreement, approved by the RHA, which provides that any act of a member of the practice with respect to the allotted sum binds the other members of the practice. Where practices group together for the purposes of applying for GP fundholding practice status, it will be important that they have clear understandings, in written form, as to how decisions in the fundholding practice are to be made, its management and administration.

Time of application

Recognition as a fundholding practice takes effect from 1 April and application for recognition has to be made by 1 April in the preceding year.

Determination of application

The RHA is required to send to each member of the practice notice of and reasons for its decision. Where it has refused recognition, it must inform each member of the practice of the right to appeal to the Secretary of State against that refusal.

Appeals to the Secretary of State

Any appeal to the Secretary of State where recognition has been refused must be made within one month, beginning with the date on which notice of the RHA's decision was sent to the members of the practice. The presumption is likely to be that the date of the RHA's notice is the date that it was sent, but it would be sensible to keep a note of the date the notice is received and the post-mark on the letter, in case any dispute subsequently arises as to when time began to run for the purposes of calculating the period in which the appeal has to be made.

The notice of appeal must be signed by all the members of the practice and contain a concise statement of the grounds of appeal on which the practice relies. The Secretary of State will send a copy of the notice to the RHA.

The 1993 Regulations have given the Secretary of State a new power. Where in any case it appears to her just and proper to do so she may dispense with the requirement that the notice of appeal be signed by all the members of the practice or extend the time limit of one month for sending the notice of appeal.

The Secretary of State can decide the appeal on the basis of written representations, if she considers it can properly be determined without an oral hearing. If she decides that an oral hearing is required, then she will appoint one or more persons to hear the appeal. She will take into consideration the report of the person, or persons, hearing the appeal when making her decision.

Conditions for continuing recognition

Having achieved fundholding status, the practice has to fulfil various conditions if it is to continue to be entitled to recognition. Apart from continuing compliance with the conditions for original recognition, there are conditions relating to the maintenance of a fundholding account for receipt of and payments from the allotted sum and the provision of information and accounts to the relevant FHSA. There are restrictions on demanding or accepting payments (including payments in kind) for treatment of patients except in certain specified circumstances. There are obligations to ensure that employees of the practice and providers to it of services are suitably competent.

The goods and services which may be purchased with the allotted sum, other than general medical services, are specified in a list approved by the Secretary of State. Amongst the conditions that have to be observed by a fundholding practice is one that none of these goods or services shall be purchased for a patient of a member of the practice 'from any provider with which any member of the practice is connected', unless:

- the RHA has consented in writing to the purchase of those goods or services from that provider, or

- it is impracticable, having regard to the condition of the patient, to obtain the consent and no alternative provider is available, or

- the provider is a health service body other than a fundholding practice.

The 1993 Regulations define in some detail when a member of a fundholding practice shall be treated as connected with a provider. Such a connection exists if a member:

- is employed by or is a close relative of a person employed by the provider,

- where the provider is a company he is a director of the company or a partner of or employed by or a close relative of a person who is a director of the company,

- he is in partnership with or is a close relative of a person who is in partnership with the provider,

- where the provider is a fundholding practice, he is a close relative of a member of the practice

- where the provider is an individual, he is a close relative of that individual

- he has a beneficial interest in the securities of the provider (eg where shares in a company are held in his name or by his nominee), or

- he provides or has provided any services to that provider

'Close relative' for these purposes means a husband, wife, brother, sister, father, mother, son or daughter.

The 1993 Regulations prohibit the RHA from consenting to a

purchase from a provider with which a member of the practice is connected unless it is satisfied that no member of the practice will receive any payment from the allotted sum, whether directly or indirectly, which is wholly or mainly attributable to treatment given to patients of the practice. This provision is aimed in particular at the ploy adopted by some fundholders of forming a limited company to provide services. The 1993 Regulations also introduce a new provision, referred to below, allowing fundholders to be paid from the fund for the provision of certain diagnostic tests and surgical procedures. Given this concession, the NHSME considers that contracts between fundholders and third parties, such as limited companies, are no longer necessary or, presumably, justified. An example of an indirect payment out of the fund would be the payment of a salary or dividend to a member of the practice who was a director or shareholder of a company providing services to the practice. Whether or not it was wholly or mainly attributable to treatment given to patients of the practice would be a matter of fact and degree.

Additions to existing fundholding practices

If a medical practitioner wishes to join an existing fundholding practice, then he and the members of the existing fundholding practice would have to make a new application to the relevant RHA for recognition. The provisions regarding the time of application and the effective date of recognition would not apply to such an application. However, the requirement to make an application does not apply to a medical practitioner who becomes a partner of a member of the fundholding practice as a result of the grant of a successful application by him to an FHSA under Regulation 5 of the National Health Service (General Medical Services) Regulations 1992 (application for inclusion in the medical list or to succeed to a vacancy).

On giving written notice to the RHA he will be treated as a member of the fundholding practice, although he did not join in the original application.

Withdrawal or death of a member of a fundholding practice

Where a member of a fundholding practice withdraws from a practice or dies its recognition will not be affected by the withdrawal, or death provided the conditions for recognition continue to be fulfilled. However, a member who is a partner of another member of the practice cannot withdraw, unless he also ceases to be the partner of the member remaining in the practice.

Renunciation of recognition

A majority of members of a fundholding practice may renounce recognition with effect from 31 March by sending notice of their intention to do so to the relevant RHA. What is meant by a majority is not defined in the Regulations. Presumably, it is a majority of individual members of the practice, rather than of partnerships, where a fundholding practice consists of a grouping of practices. Where there is such a group, this question of renunciation of recognition is another matter which should be addressed when the group are considering the ground rules to apply to relations between themselves.

The notice of renunciation has to be in writing and signed by a majority of the members of the fundholding practice. It must be sent at least one month before the 31 March following the sending of the notice. It will be important, therefore, to be conscious of the deadline for giving the notice, otherwise the practice may have to continue for another year. Adequate time should be allowed to prepare the notice, as it has to be accompanied by a statement containing particulars of:

- the NHS contracts into which the fundholding practice has entered
- the amount standing in the fundholding account (presumably at the date the notice is given)

- the amount standing in the fundholding account which may be applied by way of savings from the allotted sum

- the liabilities of the members of the practice.

As from the 31 March stated in the notice, the practice will cease to be a recognized fundholding practice. It will, however, be required to fulfil certain conditions regarding the fundholding account and the allotted sum until the RHA is satisfied that all the liabilities of the former fundholding practice have been discharged.

Once the RHA is satisfied that all the liabilities have been discharged, it will give notice to that effect to each member of the former fundholding practice. If, after renunciation, no part of the allotted sum remains in the fundholding account, but the liabilities of the practice have not been discharged, then the RHA can transfer all the rights and liabilities of the practice to itself. Where the liabilities have been discharged and there are still monies in the fundholding account, then the practice may apply that sum only for the prescribed purposes to which savings from the allotted sum can be put, ie broadly for the purpose of providing more and better service for patients by the purchase of materials or equipment and the improvement of premises.

Removal of recognition

The discretion to remove recognition is given to the relevant RHA in two situations.

1. Where, by 28 February in any year, the RHA has notified the members of the practice of the amount of the allotted sum for the financial year beginning on 1 April and the members of the practice have not within one month beginning with the date that the RHA's notice is sent, notified it that they accept that amount as their allotted sum. The 1993 Regulations contemplate that the notice removing recognition will take effect on 1 April succeeding it, as the provisions on procedure for removing recognition state that

the removal has effect from 1 April following the sending of the notice. If the RHA does not notify the allotted sum until the last possible minute, ie 28 February, and then has to wait for one month, it will have virtually no time to send the notice removing recognition from 1 April. There is a right of appeal to the Secretary of State against removal of recognition on these grounds.

2. The RHA may also remove recognition if any of the conditions for continuing recognition is no longer fulfilled in relation to the practice. This notice can be given at any time, but removal of recognition has to take effect at least three months from the date that the notice is sent. There are detailed provisions in the 1993 Regulations regarding the making of representations to the RHA, orally or in writing, by members of the practice in response to such a notice and of the right of appeal to the Secretary of State.

Removal of recognition with immediate effect

Where any of the conditions for continuing recognition is no longer fulfilled in relation to the practice the RHA is required to remove recognition with immediate effect where it appears to the RHA that it is necessary either:

• in the interests of patients of members of the practice; or

• for the purposes of ensuring proper management of the allotted sum.

There is a right of appeal to the Secretary of State.

Consequences of removal

On the day that removal of recognition takes effect, all the rights and liabilities of the fundholding practice transfer to the RHA. It may also deal with the allotted sum as though it was the fundholding practice, except for any savings from the allotted sum made by the practice which the RHA shall apply for such of the purposes permitted by the 1993 Regulations as the former fundholding practice may require.

Allotted sum – authorized purposes

There are detailed provisions in Regulations 19 to 24 of the 1993 Regulations dealing with the purposes for which the allotted sum may be applied.

From 1 April 1993 the Hospital and Community Health Services elements of the GP fundholding scheme are extended to include:

- district nursing
- health visiting
- chiropody
- dietetics
- all community and out-patient mental health services
- mental health counselling
- health services for people with a learning disability
- referrals made by health visitors, district nurses and community mental handicap nurses.

The Yellow Book (EL(92)48) and Supplementary guidance (HSG(92)53) identify the fact that legally *'once a service has been added to the list of goods and services which fundholders purchase, it becomes their purchasing responsibility and the DHA has no jurisdiction to purchase these services on behalf of fundholders' patients'*. That does not preclude collaboration with other purchasers using joint contracts.

Changes made by the 1993 Regulations from those they succeed include the following:

- the requirement that the allotted sum is to be used to purchase goods and services, other than general medical services, on the list approved by the Secretary of State, as are necessary for the proper treatment of individuals on the lists of patients of the members of the practice, has been extended by the addition of the words '*and are appropriate in all the circumstances having regard, in particular, to the needs of all those individuals*'

- there is an obligation on fundholding practices to enter into at least one NHS contract for the purchase of district nursing and health visiting services either in combination or separately. The consent of the RHA is required to any such NHS contract which has to be with an established health authority or NHS Trust. It is not the intention that practices should provide community nursing services through their own employees or by contracting with private providers

- in connection with the payment of salaries the allotted sum may only be applied for the purpose of paying the salaries of those who are employed:
  - to provide treatment to the patients of the members of the practice, or
  - in connection with the management or administration of the practice
- suitably qualified competent and experienced medical practitioners who are members of the practice can now be paid out of the fund for the provision of certain diagnostic tests and surgical procedures for patients of the practice. The permitted services are specified in Schedule 3 of the 1993 Regulations. The written consent of the RHA is required to any such arrangements and it has to be satisfied that various criteria set out in the 1993 Regulations will be met. Guidance on these new provisions and on the provision of services through other health care professionals for patients of the practice are contained in HSG (93)14-GP fundholding practices: the provision of secondary care

- there are new provisions giving powers to the RHA to recover sums misapplied by members of the practice

- the provision dealing with the application of savings from the allotted sum has been expanded to make it clear that in making their purchasing decisions (including payments of salaries and payments to members of the practice for Schedule 3 services) the members of the practice can take into account the possible benefit to all their patients of making savings.

NHS contracts

Fundholders will place contracts with provider units, be they a directly managed unit (DMU) or NHS trust. In the case of a DMU, as it has no separate legal personality, the contract will be with its District Health Authority (DHA).

The 1990 Act creates a new species of contract for which there are no obvious parallels in English law, called an NHS contract. Section 4 of the Act defines an NHS contract as meaning *'an arrangement under which one health service body ('the acquirer') arranges for the provision to it by another health service body ('the provider') of goods or services which it reasonably requires for the purposes of its functions'*. 'Health service body' for this purpose includes health authorities, FHSAs, NHS trusts and fundholding practices.

It is important to appreciate that it is the intention that NHS contracts should not be contracts in the proper legal sense, even if they look like any other commercial contract. Section 4(3) of the 1990 Act provides that if an NHS contract were to be a contract in law, it shall not be regarded for any purpose as giving rise to contractual rights or liabilities. The justification for this provision is that as NHS contracts are agreements between publicly funded bodies, Ministers do not consider it right for disputes between health service bodies to be susceptible to litigation in the Courts. Section 4(3) attempts to preclude this possibility. Whether that attempt has been successful is a matter for debate and the Courts will look closely at provisions ousting their jurisdiction. For example, any determination by the Secretary of State of a dispute about an NHS contract referred to her is likely to be capable of being subject to judicial review.

Resolution of disputes

As the intention is that recourse cannot be had to the Courts, either party can refer a dispute in connection with an NHS contract to the Secretary of State for determination. The 1990 Act also introduces another novel concept, which is the procedure for resolving precontractual disputes. A party to a proposed NHS contract can refer the terms of that proposed contract to the Secretary of State for determination. It has to demonstrate that the terms proposed in the negotiations by the other party are unfair, because the other party is seeking to take advantage of its position as the only, or the only practicable provider, or by reason of any other unequal bargaining position. Or where terms cannot be agreed for any other reason arising out of the relative bargaining position of the prospective parties. An example of where an unequal bargaining position might be regarded as existing would be if a purchaser threatened to stop purchasing services from the provider, or a provider threatened to cease supplying them to the purchaser, if its terms were not agreed, where there was no alternative practical provider or purchaser. Guidance from the NHS Management Executive on the subject of resolving disputes places much emphasis on the parties endeavouring to resolve contractual disputes locally and that the formal disputes procedure is really a matter of last resort.

In the case of pre-contractual disputes, the parties are expected to seek the assistance of their Regional General Manager(s) as conciliator(s). The function of a conciliator is to try and bring the parties together to reach an amicable compromise and normally he would not be expected to have powers of decision – unlike an arbitrator.

Referral of dispute to Secretary of State

Where a pre-contractual dispute or a dispute about an existing NHS contract has been referred to the Secretary of State, the intention is that she will normally appoint an independent adjudicator to act on her behalf. The proposal is that the adjudicators will be drawn from a panel composed of senior NHS managers nominated by each Region. Those managers will be employees of the Region, the DHA or an NHS trust.

The person appointed as adjudicator can invite the parties to make oral in addition to written observations and can also consult experts. There are time limits set out in the National Health Service Contracts (Dispute Resolution) Regulations 1991 for the various stages in the dispute resolution procedure, it being the intention that disputes be settled without delay.

Decisions by adjudicators are binding on both parties and wide powers are given by the 1990 Act to the Secretary of State, or the adjudicator appointed by her, including the power to vary the terms of the NHS contract, or bring it to an end. In the case of pre-contractual disputes he may specify terms to be included in the proposed NHS contract and may direct that it be proceeded with. In both situations, therefore, there are powers to impose a contract on an unwilling party.

Contractual arbitration

Parties to an NHS contract are encouraged to include provisions in their contract for agreed arbitration if a party believes that the contract has been broken, including specifying the arbitrator in the contract and the terms on which arbitration may take place. The relevant Guidelines suggest that the arbitrator should usually be their Regional General Manager. However, the inclusion of an arbitration clause in the contract does not preclude a party from invoking the statutory disputes resolution procedure.

The Guidelines also indicate that the presumption in determining a dispute under the statutory procedure is likely to be that the outcome will give effect to the agreement which was originally reached, rather than a new agreement which the parties should have reached. It is therefore important that the contract is as clear as possible from the outset. In the case of a contract enforceable in law, which an NHS contract is not, a Court or an arbitrator looks at the express terms of the contract, but other terms may be implied by law, eg that a person who supplies services will carry them out with reasonable care and skill. Also, in the case of a legal contract there are statutory restrictions on the use of certain clauses, such as exemption clauses. As NHS contracts are not to be regarded as contracts enforceable by law, it would seem to follow that these implied terms or statutory restrictions will not apply and the adjudicator will have to rely solely on the express terms of the contract.

Contracts with the private sector

Although contracts with other health service bodies are not legally enforceable, those with the private sector will be enforceable. The form of an NHS contract may not be appropriate when a fundholding practice is contracting with the private sector for the provision of services.

Conclusions

In the checklist of items to be considered when applying for, or considering applying for, fundholding status, should be a review of agreements. The review should cover both existing agreements and what new agreements may be needed if fundholding status is obtained.

Partnership agreement

The existing partnership agreement should be reviewed to see what changes may be needed to accommodate the new fundholding status. For example:

- is there an obligation on partners not to withdraw from the medical list?

- are all the partners treated as principals in the practice?

- what assets owned by the individual partners will be available to the fundholding practice?

- does an application for fundholding status require the unanimous consent of partners – certainly all will have to sign the application

- does the decision to renounce recognition as a fundholding practice require the unanimous consent of the partners, although notice of renunciation to the RHA only needs to be signed by a majority of the members of the practice?

- what happens if a partner wishes to withdraw as a member of the fundholding practice, given that in those circumstances he cannot remain a partner? Do the provisions for purchase of the share of the outgoing partner need to be reviewed? Would the valuation of that share take into account any savings from the allotted sum available to the practice?

- how much notice does a partner have to give of his wish to withdraw from the fundholding practice?

- are any restrictive covenants on outgoing partners adequate to cover the situation of a withdrawal by a member from a fundholding practice, or, indeed enforceable in those circumstances?

Grouping of practices

Where a group of separate practices wishes to make an application for fundholding status, they should certainly consider entering into a written agreement between themselves, dealing with points similar to those which would be covered by a partnership agreement. In particular, thought should be given to the limits of authority of individual members of the fundholding practice. It will be recalled that a condition of recognition by the RHA is that the members of the practice have entered into an agreement which provides that any act of a member with respect to the allotted sum binds the other members. If the fundholding practice is to employ additional staff or ancillary services, how are these salaries and costs to be split between members? How are payments out of the allotted sum to be applied between the different practices making up the fundholding practice?

Consortia

Responsibilities of the various participants in GP fundholding consortia should be clearly defined in writing, including details of what contingency arrangements need to be made if practices want to withdraw from the consortium and the procedure for such withdrawal (including the notice that has to be given).

Employment contracts

The opportunity should be taken to review employment contracts and consider what new employment contracts may be needed for staff who will be employed in the fundholding practice.

NHS contracts

Once fundholding status is obtained, then the practice will have to enter into NHS contracts with its providers. The form of those contracts may initially be dictated by the provider, but the fundholding practice should consider what provisions it expects to see in the contracts and seek additions or amendments where appropriate. There may, for example, be room for fundholders to negotiate on matters such as:

- waiting times
- level of staff treating patients
- timescale within which out-patients should be seen
- format for referral letters.

No doubt account will also be taken of the Patient's Charter.

10

Information Technology: Implications for Fundholders

Nicola Amery

Introduction

The fundholding initiative will make substantial and varied demands on all members of the primary health care team, not least those within general practice. These demands stem not only from the still relative newness of the scheme, with its own terminology and disciplines, but also from the need to introduce appropriate management and administrative systems to cope with the volume of data being recorded and processed.

The consequent impact of information technology must not be underestimated, yet a clear sense of perspective must also be maintained about the limitations of computer systems and their true role within the fundholding process. This chapter attempts to clarify that role and to identify some of the issues involved in the implementation of fundholding systems within general practice.

The Department of Health specification

Much has been made of the 'strictness' of the computer software specification produced by Hoskins on behalf of the Department of Health. It is, therefore, worth shedding some light on this area, if only to dispel some of the mystery which appears to surround it. The Requirements Specification, which has had a number of major revisions, is now a document of over 200 pages, containing details of functionality, data structures, coding and validation, security controls and audit trails.

From a functional point of view, it is a generic specification. This means that the variations which are visible between software packages, are in most cases, determined by operating environments and the overall approach of the particular system suppliers. Most, if not all, the major suppliers have been subjected to the rigours of conformance test procedures, which were designed to ensure that the systems adhered to the functional requirements of the specification. There are, however, areas which are open to interpretation and it might prove an interesting exercise to re-run the conformance tests in the light of the various interim enhancements which have been made to each software package.

The basic functions revolve around certain accounting procedures within a series of ledgers.

1. The financial (nominal) ledger is at the core of the system and records transactions for the following:

   • income (budgets) for hospital services, prescribing, staff, community services etc

   • expenditure during the year (FIEA)

   • savings allocations

   • balance sheet (double-entry bookkeeping method) for current assets, liabilities, GP current account, FHSA account

   • cash payments (F1 account).

2. The referrals ledger is used to record both accounting and clinical details of each fundholding referral. This has given rise to varying degrees of 'integration' among different systems.

3. The purchase ledger deals with the recording and payment of suppliers' invoices, although for the sake of simplicity some suppliers have incorporated this facility within the nominal ledger.

In addition to these primary accounting transactions, there is also a requirement for expenditure and cash flow forecasting, albeit in approximation which manifests itself, in most systems, in the form of a simple spreadsheet.

Finally, the vast quantities of data which are recorded in the system produce the inevitable reams of paper as a result of the statutory reporting requirements. There are over 30 of these standard reports covering referrals, financial schedules and fore- casting statements. The content and format of each of these reports has been defined in detail by the specification to enable easier analysis by outside bodies such as the FHSA. However simplicity and artistic design have not been borne in mind, although some of these can now be exported electronically to FHSAs, or indeed other spreadsheets for further analysis. Some further exploration of these reports would therefore be recom- mended during the period of systems training and implementa- tion.

From this overview, it should be clear that the emphasis of the fundholding software looks towards accounting rather than practice management functions, although there is much within the specification which lends itself usefully to the general man- agement of certain aspects of fundholding. These include mon- itoring referral costs, referral rates, patient costs, waiting times etc. The possibility of electronic links between GP, FHSA and hospital also makes a valuable overall contribution. Maximum benefit however, can only be derived from sensible preparation and planning and appreciation of the fundholding system as an integral part of the practice's overall information technology (IT) strategy.

Preparation and planning systems

In most Regions, Health Authorities have been given consider- able guidance on the preparations for fundholding, although advice on computer systems was variable. Clearly, one area of emphasis in preparatory years is the collection of referral statis- tics in order to assess current activity levels and help in contract negotiations. The nature and scope of these statistics varied enormously from Region to Region and consequently different methods of collecting the data are recommended. Ideally, these data should be collected over a whole year to provide for seasonal variations and the most obvious source of such data would be a general practice computer. This may be a fundholding system, a clinical management system, a combination of both or indeed a bespoke system specifically designed for the purpose. The value of computer collated data, however, does depend on the nature of the data set stipulated by each Region, as well as the appropriateness of the existing computer. Perhaps the most important issue is the 'quality' of the data which has been/can be collected in the practice over an extended period of time. Any computer user will be familiar with the adage 'garbage in, garbage out', which becomes even more pertinent if the practice is to use computer-held data as the basis for financial decision making and business planning. In theory, those practices which were recording information for the Data Research Schemes should be well disciplined in this respect.

One of the prerequisites of the fundholding initiative is that participating practices should have 'adequate' levels of computerization. This may or may not include consulting room screens, depending on the set-up and management structures which are already in place. Yet, part of the success of fundholding lies in how well the facilities are developed to cope with the extra commitment imposed by the scheme.

As already mentioned, a considerable volume of paperwork is generated through the daily processes of referrals and invoices as well as the monthly and ad hoc reports. Experience has shown that the ideal team to administer all aspects of fundholding should include, as well as the business/fund manager, a computer operator, who will be responsible for generating and processing referrals. Office logistics are therefore important and the planning period should include preparation of the computer location. Thought should also be given to providing space not only for the computer but also for photocopier, fax machine, filing cabinets and so on. The fundholding computer will provide the focal point for the fundholding administration processes, but information will have to be gleaned from a number of areas both from within the practice as well as outside bodies. The data flow might best be demonstrated as in Figure 10.1.

Much of the clinical data which initiates the fundholding referral should be collected by the clinical management computer. If it is not, then provision must be made for manual recording and collection.

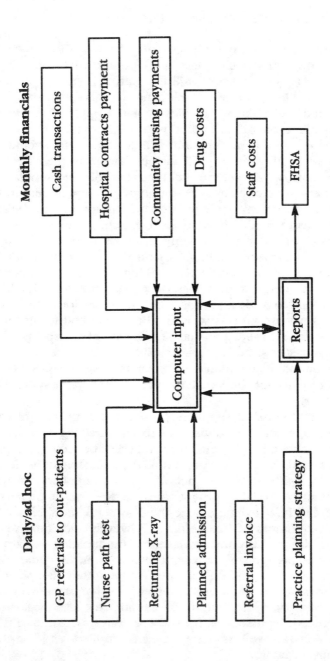

Monthly financials

Cash transactions

Hospital contracts payment

Community nursing payments

Drug costs

Staff costs

FHSA

Daily/ad hoc

GP referrals to out-patients

Nurse path test

Returning X-ray

Planned admission

Referral invoice

Practice planning strategy

Computer input

Reports

Figure 10.1: Data flow.

Installation and implementation

If all the computer systems conform to the Department of Health specification which one should the practice choose?

In most cases the practice will have already been through the decision making process of selecting a practice management system and while the same rules should apply to fundholding systems, there are additional considerations which should not be ignored. Computers for fundholding cannot and should not be viewed in isolation, even if in the short term their function appears narrow. Long-term commitment of the supplier to fundholding development is as important as commitment to the clinical management system. Use of computers in general practice has expanded beyond all recognition and there seems no respite from the ever-growing demands for increased functionality and, perhaps more importantly, increased integration.

The definitions and perceptions of 'integration' are numerous and wide-ranging, but at a basic level, the direction should be towards one-step data entry. The most obvious benefit is reduced keyboard time as well as a better method for maintaining accurate and validated data. This is true of all aspects of GP computer systems, but complete valid data is at the very heart of the fundholding initiative. The underlying message, therefore, is to consider the long-term plans of a certain system and its supplier.

Although almost all suppliers profess the simplicity of their software, it would be unwise not to take training seriously. A good understanding of some basic and relevant accounting principles, including double-entry bookkeeping, should be fundamental to this training period. Most suppliers provide comprehensive training programmes on the use of their own systems and how to implement those systems most effectively within the context of fundholding. However, additional advice on the wider implications and issues of fundholding will always by useful. This type of broader training should include some suggested mechanisms of data collection within the practice, the preparation of standard data, eg hospital references and contracts as well as internal procedures for data validation. These generic courses are provided in certain areas by FHSAs and Regions as well as some system suppliers and they are worth investigating.

Conclusion

Perhaps the most extraordinary aspect of fundholding to date is the enormous variation between Regions in their approach to computerization and the consequent policies and recommendations which have been put in place. This may be because of the high-profile nature of the scheme and the levels of reimbursement for computer purchases have undoubtedly exacerbated this. However, why rush to install a fundholding computer? Apart from the obvious political and monetary influences, there is a clear need for practices to implement additional management systems and the computer is one of these. The successful introduction of any new system and particularly a computer system, requires discipline, concentration and, more than anything else, a lot of time.

Fundholding is still in comparative infancy and while the learning curve is very steep it is often underestimated. The controls which are inherent in the software application will be new to most practices, yet by their very nature will assist in the overall implementation of fundholding. The sooner the system is in place, the better chance practices will have to really get to grips with new procedures and management structures.

11

Financial Management: Accounting Considerations

Laurence Slavin

The introduction of fundholding is a new challenge for medical practitioners. GPs have always been considered as businessmen (at least by their advisers and the Inland Revenue), and operated in a business environment. However, the 1990 Contract forced GPs to look more critically at the financial aspects of running their practice, and this has been taken one stage further with the introduction of fundholding.

Fundholding was initially known as budget holding. The change in the term was made mainly for political purposes, as budgets indicate a limit of funds rather than funds being led by demand. This concept is discussed later. During the rest of this chapter the term 'budgets' rather than funds is used as this is the more accurate description.

This chapter covers:

- what is meant by a budget?
- control of the budget
- the role of the accountant
- variance analysis
- the management fee.

What is meant by a budget?

It is worth highlighting the function of a budget – it combines the concepts of authority and responsibility. Thus designating someone a budget-holder for certain types of expenditure gives them the authority to incur expenditure against the budget without higher reference. Alongside the authority is the responsibility placed on the budget-holder to contain overall expenditure and to use resources effectively and efficiently. Thus a fundholding practice will have increased freedom of action coupled with increased responsibility.

A budget is the formal outlining of objectives, and their means of attainment. Budgets require management planning, provide definite expectations and promote communication and co-ordination.

In terms of the fundholding practice, the setting of objectives is the establishment of the drugs budget, the staffing levels and the referral patterns. The means of attainment is the negotiated budget.

Control of the budget

Control of the budget is vital to the success of the scheme. Budgetary control involves five main functions.

1. **Planning**: establishment of a budget team that will typically include some or all of the partners, a practice/budget manager, a data collection clerk and the practice accountant.

2. **Communication**: ensuring all members of the practice understand the objectives and the means to achieve them.

3. **Motivation**: encouraging all members of the practice to achieve the outlined objectives.

4. **Comparison**: comparison of actual with planned results. This is the area where accountants can play a most useful role.

5. **Action**: when events do not conform to plan, corrective action needs to be taken. Another area where the accountant can have a key role.

The role of the accountant

Planning

The accountant will have a considered opinion on the financial abilities of the practice through his work as the practice accountant. He will understand the general attitude of the practice towards finance, and will be able to guide the practice through areas they may find difficult to accept. The accountant will know where the practice and practice staff have weaknesses in relation to bookkeeping and accounting and will be able to predict likely problems in the staff's ability to run a fundholding practice.

Communication and Motivation

The accountant is the 'business' person most closely associated with the practice. He will be able to advise the practice on the effectiveness and importance of communication and motivation.

Comparison

The comparison of the budget to the actual results is critical to the success of the scheme. A possible overspend must be reported as soon as possible to allow the practice to either change working practises, or to approach the Regional Health Authority for additional funds. The software supplied to the practice will provide comprehensive reports indicating the progress of the budget on a monthly basis. Understanding these reports and drawing the correct conclusions is an area where the accountant should play an important role.

Action

The effectiveness of the action taken will depend on the speed and accuracy with which conclusions and reports can be prepared. The accountant should play a key role in this area.

A project team consisting of a lead partner, the fundholding/ practice manager and the accountant should be set up with clear tasks and deadlines to steer fundholding in the practice.

This team should meet regularly. For example, the monthly reports could be produced on the second Monday of the following month, the accountant assists in drawing conclusions on the following Wednesday, and a meeting with the partners held on the Thursday. A named individual should be placed in charge of the team to ensure its effective operation. This will usually be the fundholding/practice manager.

Budgeting techniques

Variance analysis

A key technique in budgetary control is variance analysis. In simple terms, a variance is a variation from budget.

It may be budgeted, for instance, that the practice will refer four hip replacement operations per month at a budgeted cost of £2,000 each. If the practice actually refers three hip operations at £2,700 each then the practice has an overall unfavourable variance of £100.

This however only provides limited information. Variance analysis can be used to provide further information. An overall variance can be further broken down between price variances and efficiency variances. The price variance explains the difference between actual unit price and budgeted price. The efficiency variance shows the difference between the units that should have been used and the units that were actually used. The formulas for calculating these variances are as follows.

Price variance

(Difference in unit price of inputs) × actual inputs used = price variance

Efficiency variance

(Difference in units used) × standard unit price = efficiency variance

Taking the example above, the price variance can be calculated as follows: £700 × three operations = £2,100 unfavourable variance.

The efficiency variance can be calculated as follows: One hip operation × £2,000 = £2,000 favourable variance.

To summarize:

Price variance (unfavourable)	(£2,100)
Efficiency variance (favourable)	£2,000
Overall variance (unfavourable)	(£100)

Therefore an overall variance of £100 that may have been ignored as being immaterial actually warrants further action when analysed further. The reason for the unfavourable price variances requires explanation and may justify an increase in the budget, the favourable efficiency variance should count towards a potential underspend.

Management fee

Some consideration should be given to the accounting treatment of the management fee of £17,500 in the preparatory year and the annual management fee of £35,500. The guidance from the GMSC is specific. The management fee should not be netted off against the expense but shown separately as income. This causes no problem for revenue related expenditure such as consultancy fees, locums or other services purchased with the management allowance, as the net effect in the profit and loss account will be nil. Where, however, the management fee is used for capital expenditure, the management fee will be shown in the profit and loss account and therefore subject to income tax in full, while the asset is shown in the balance sheet with only 25% of the cost allowed as a deduction from the profits on a reducing balance basis. For example, £10,000 of the management allowance used to purchase computer equipment will be treated as follows:

Year 1

Taxable income – management allowance	£10,000
Allowable expenditure (25% of cost)	£2,500
Taxable surplus	£7,500
Tax payable on the surplus at (say) 40%	£3,000

Year 2

Taxable income	–
Allowable expenditure (25% on written down balance)	£1,875
Deficit available for tax relief	£1,875
Tax saved on deficit at (say) 40%	£750

Year 3

Taxable income	–
Allowable expenditure (25% on written down value)	£1,406
Deficit available for tax relief	£1,406
Tax saved on deficit at (say) 40%	£562

Year 4

Taxable income	–
Allowable expenditure (25% on written down value)	£1,054
Deficit available for tax relief	£1,054
Tax saved on deficit at (say) 40%	£421

Year 5

Taxable income	–
Allowable expenditure (25% on written down value)	£791
Deficit available for tax relief	£791
Tax saved on deficit at (say) 40%	£316

Summary

Year 1 tax paid	£3,000
Year 2 tax reclaimed	(£750)
Year 3 tax reclaimed	(£562)
Year 4 tax reclaimed	(£421)
Year 5 tax reclaimed	(£316)
Tax still not reclaimed	£951

If the accounting treatment had been to net off the management allowance against the cost, the effect would have been as follows:

Year 1

Cost of computer equipment	£10,000
Less reimbursement	(£10,000)
Surplus/deficit to be taxed/tax relieved	–

No tax payable/no tax relief due.

It is therefore in the interests of the practice to net the allowance against the expenditure to which it relates. Although this may be in contravention of the directions given by the GMSC, there is a good precedent for adopting such an approach. Statements of Standard Accounting Practice (SSAPs) are issued by the accountancy bodies, as best practice to be adopted by practising accountants. SSAP4, The Accounting Treatment of Government Grants, gives the following guidance: *'If the grant (reimbursement) is revenue is nature, (ie relates to an expense charged in the profit and loss account) then the grant (reimbursement) should be included in the same period as the expenditure.*

If the grant (reimbursement) is capital in nature, then the grant can either be set against the cost of the asset, or by setting up the reimbursement as a liability, and allocating this to the profit and loss account on the basis as the asset is depreciated. Whichever of these two treatments is adopted, it should be clear that it would be incorrect to allocate the reimbursement to the profit and loss account when the asset remains in the balance sheet.'

Therefore practices should be advised it will be clearly in their interest to avoid following the directions given by the GMSC and to follow the treatment in SSAP4.

Some consideration needs to be given to the possibility of an underspend on the annual budget. In the writer's opinion, long term substantial savings are unlikely to be received, however some initial savings may be possible. Those savings can only be used in the year in which the savings are audited. This will be the year following the year in which the savings were made. For example, if a saving of £100,000 is saved in 1993/94, it will be audited and confirmed in 1994/95. It can only be used to pay for debts incurred in 1994/95. It cannot be used to pay off a loan incurred in 1993/94.

Careful planning needs to be given to the strategic direction of the practice. If a substantial underspend is forecast, then at the earliest opportunity, the practice needs to plan how to utilize this, for example, how it can be used to reduce the borrowings necessary in a cost rent scheme. The practice accountant, who by his very role will have a working overview of the practice should be able to advise on these matters.

A more difficult question is whether an underspend is taxable. As the underspend cannot be converted into cash, paying tax on a saving that may be difficult to realize would be most unwelcome.

The GP fundholders' manual of accounts mentions that the funding for hospital services, drugs, staff expenses and other non-capital expenditure is taxable income, but the expenses to which it relates are tax deductable. Underspends are therefore taxable, but if the underspend is used to purchase further services (revenue expenditure) the expenditure is matched against the underspend netting off any effect. If the underspend is used to purchase capital expenditure the manual of accounts recommends that the income be netted off against the cost of the asset, in much the same way as the management allowance is described above. There is however a difference. The manual of accounts states on the same page that an underspend must, by definition, be a surplus of taxable income. If a surplus of taxable income is used to purchase capital expenditure, then the income is taxed immediately, and the asset will be eligible for capital allowance. The underspend cannot be described as a capital based grant (as in SSAP4 above) and therefore the practice may find themselves having to pay tax out of funds which are denied to them.

The guidance given in the manual of accounts for such problems is 'specific points should be discussed with the Tax Inspector responsible for the practice'. This would be unwise, and it should fall to the Department of Health to agree a statement of practice with the Board of Inland Revenue.

Summary

From the initial assessment of the practice's ability to manage a budget, to extrapolating information from reports, to advising on the tax position of the practice's fund, the practice accountant should have a key role to play in the fundholding practice.

12

What is a Consortium?

Peter Smith and Jeremy Harris

As fundholding has developed, groups of GPs around the country have begun to form larger purchasing collectives. It was not until December 1992 that the NHS Management Executive (NHSME) issued guidelines on what it considered to be the acceptable face of co-operatives. This brief tour around the consortium maze is based on the multifund model developed by Dr Jeremy Harris and Dr Peter Smith for the GPs of Kingston and Richmond in Surrey, because it fulfils all the criteria of the NHSME guidelines.

What is a fundholding consortium?

A fundholding consortium is a group of two or more existing or prospective individual funds acting together in the management of their budgets. This definition includes several important terms:

A group: this does not have to be a formal arrangement, but is probably stronger for being so.

Existing or prospective: the definition has to include those GPs who are intending setting up consortia. Experience has shown that purchasers take such groups very seriously from an early stage, even before they have any legal status.

Acting together in the management: This is an essential part of the definition of a consortium, excluding such bodies as the National Association of Fundholding Practices (NAFP), where a consensus view may prevail, but has no direct effect on the management of individual budgets.

Budgets: the plural term is crucial. Since the introduction of fundholding, the term 'consortium' has been erroneously applied to multipractice funds, or 'groupies', where practices apply jointly for fundholding status in order to achieve the 7,000 patients necessary to qualify for fundholding. Unfortunately, where two or three practices are gathered together, there is not necessarily a consortium in the midst of them. Unless they hold more than one fund between them, they will have no greater influence than any other singleton fund.

What is not a consortium?

A multipractice fund is *not* a consortium. No matter how many practices are gathered together under the umbrella of a single budget, it remains a 'groupie' or multipractice fund.

Despite the appearance of various purchasing groups around the country, only District Health Authorities (DHAs), Family Health Services Authorities (FHSAs), Health Commissions and GP fundholders have any legal status in the purchasing and commissioning of health care. Other groups do not have any *statutory* responsibility for the funds they control and should therefore not be termed consortia. To avoid confusion, where 'consortium' is used throughout the remainder of this chapter, it refers to a *fundholding* consortium.

Why are consortia necessary?

Consortia have been around since the early days of fundholding. Initially, they were useful merely as a forum for developing the *concept* of fundholding, and to ensure that fundholders within the same area benefited from shared experience. It is not surprising, therefore that some consortia have now outlived their usefulness and are now in the process of amicable disintegration.

As successive annual waves of fundholders have appeared, fears have arisen amongst some GPs that the minimum list size stipulation of 7,000 patients would exclude smaller practices from the scheme, and that larger practices would be deterred by the amount of work involved. It has become apparent that DHA contracts allow little flexibility to individual practices and tend to be completed by providers early in the financial year, leaving significant periods when, for example, cold surgery has to be postponed. There is therefore a possibility that a differential level of care could develop between patients of non-fundholders, served by DHA contracts, and fundholders, served by contracts arranged to suit the needs of their practice population. By joining the fundholding scheme within a consortium, practices can minimize possible care differentials and take advantage of the flexibility that fundholding contracting allows.

Within a consortium it is also possible to pool Management Allowances to employ high quality staff with business credentials and minimize the work required. Also, the consortium allows the practices to agree on contracting issues and reduce the stress associated with competition with other practices in the same neighbourhood.

The money used to cover the fundholding budget is 'top-sliced' from the budget of the DHA. As the number of fundholders rise in any given area, the resources they control have an increasingly significant effect on the commissioning of health care within the locality. Without some form of voluntary agreement between funds (in a consortium for instance) they may end up inadvertently jeopardizing services outside the remit of fundholding.

The final reason for forming a consortium relates to the 1993 legislation that will come into force in 1996. Regional Health Authorities (RHAs) will be reduced in number, the remaining staff will become civil servants and they will become branches of the NHSME. FHSAs and DHAs will be allowed to legally merge to form a single commissioning authority.

The effect of these changes will be to remove the role of the RHA as buffer between government and commissioning agencies. The latter will then be directly answerable to the NHSME and will, for the first time, have responsibility for commissioning both secondary and primary care. Until now, FHSAs have had to deal only with primary care, and have not had to juggle with secondary care/primary care priorities. Under the new system, the needs of both will have to be balanced.

The new merged authorities will, no doubt, canvass opinions

from GPs, but they will not be obliged to act upon this information. If a large number of GPs join to form a consortium, however, their purchasing decisions directly affect any strategic view of health commissioning, and will have to be taken into account at the planning stage.

Important considerations

There are several vital factors that influence the eventual structure of a consortium.

Company and VAT law

A consortium existing as a limited company, or as a partnership, might have to charge VAT on services it offers to GPs. The glib assumption that every aspect of general practice is by definition exempt from VAT has recently been challenged. It is often not fully appreciated that VAT is levied via Customs and Excise, which is separate from the Inland Revenue, and whose deliberations are often dependent upon locally agreed dialectics of official guidelines. Nevertheless, it has been possible to draw up a legal agreement under which co-operating funds are not VAT liable. The structure that has developed is a secondary professional co-operative.

Independent contractor status

The need for GPs to remain in control of their own budgets was reflected in the form of the multifund, and was reiterated in the NHSME guidelines on consortia. Information technology links between practices and any central organization have to reflect this.

FHSA/Health Commission requirements

Most decisions regarding fundholding have now been effectively devolved from RHA to FHSA level. Hence, although there are several theoretical options, individual FHSAs might have their own ideas about the nature of any consortium.

Since it is ultimately the decision of the FHSA which practices should proceed to fundholding status, it is worthwhile working with one's local FHSA from the outset. The role of the new merged Health Commissions in fundholding has not yet been clarified.

NHS management executive guidelines

Prior to the publication of the NHSMEs guidelines, it was not clear how the Department of Health (DoH) viewed the prospect of consortia. Interestingly, they issued guidelines that synchronized with the multifund concept. Broadly speaking, their recommendations were that:

● individual funds should remain responsible both for the use of their own budgets and accountable for the delivery of national and local objectives

● separate accounts should be kept with separate in-year financial monitoring for each fund holder

● there should be agreed contingency arrangements to cover practices joining and leaving the consortium

● consortia should be able to offer economies of scale and allow individual funds to have their own input into the contracting process, basing their choices on the needs of their practice population.

Area covered

In a large consortium, areas may have different, possibly conflicting referral patterns. This fact should be recognized and separate area managers appointed to prevent conflict between fund holders.

Information technology

Information technology is the lifeblood of any consortium, and should be the very first aspect to which any steering group addresses itself.

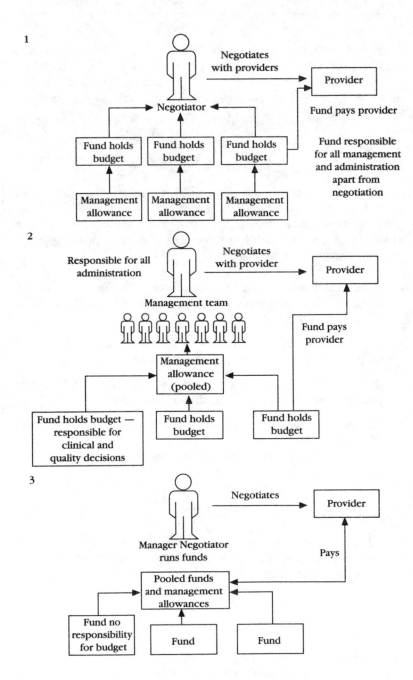

Figure 12.1: Possible structures for consortia.

Funding a multifund

Consortia should be financed from the management allowance. Some have obtained office space from DHAs, but this could possibly cause a conflict of interest in the future. The rather paltry offering of effectively half the management allowance during the preparatory year (ie the time that setup expenses are being incurred) allows no savings initially,

What possible consortia structures are there?

The three possible structures are as follows (*see* also Figure 12.1).

1. *Separate funds and separate management allowances.* Central negotiating body only (similar to the DHA) with only a loose affiliation to each other. This has the benefit that there is no legal connection for the VATman to get his teeth into, but has the disadvantage of each fund still having to do the full work of fundholding.

2. *Separate funds, pooled management allowances.* Full co-operation between fund holders with staff provided by the consortium to minimize practice workload.

3. *Pooled funds and pooled allowances.* This means the maximum loss of control for individual funds, minimum influence on their own budget and the loss of individual funds' autonomy. This arrangement does not comply with the NHSME guidelines and is potentially divisive.

How should consortium be set up?

Structure

The consortium should be set up as a secondary professional co-operative and should employ a management team consisting, for example, of a chief executive responsible for negotiation, area managers responsible for preparation of monthly reports, and data entry clerks responsible for entering information onto the individual funds' computers.

It should exist solely for itself and should provide for itself only those services that other individual funds provide for themselves. Therefore, although the individual funds will share the administrative burden, they remain responsible for the use of their own fund.

The management team will advise on all aspects of fundholding, including the use of a formulary. It will provide a forum for practices to meet and for twinning of smaller practices to take place by mutual agreement. The management allowance will mainly be used to pay the management team, as occurs in individual funds. Budgets for individual funds will be negotiated with the FHSA with due support from area and consortium managers.

Computer costs are covered by a separate reimbursement scheme. The choice of computer system is crucial and should be based on considerations of cost, quality and co-operation of computer companies.

Management team

Consortium manager
Responsible for the negotiation of budgets, contracting and for the overall performance of the management team.

Area managers
Responsible for collating information, preparing monthly reports, explaining them and advising individual funds on how best to manage their budgets.

Data entry clerks
Responsible for entering all information relating to referrals, follow-ups, procedures and all other fundholding information onto individual funds' computers.

GP input

This consists of a central committee of one representative from each fund, who then vote some of the members of their committee onto an executive board, which conveys the views on overall quality issues of the member funds to the management

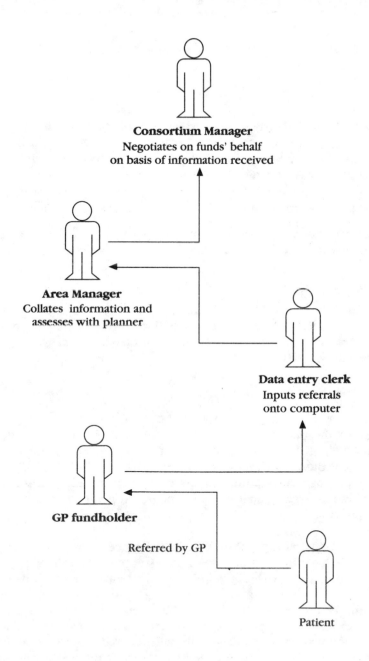

Consortium Manager
Negotiates on funds' behalf
on basis of information received

Area Manager
Collates information and
assesses with planner

Data entry clerk
Inputs referrals
onto computer

GP fundholder

Referred by GP

Patient

Figure 12.2: Overview of a possible consortium.

team and obtains information on clinical issues for its members. *See* Figure 12.2.

Premises required

Some areas have suggested DHA office space might be used to house the management team. However, to avoid conflicts of interest, office space, used solely for the purposes of fundholding, should be leased.

Legal requirements

A comprehensive legal agreement should be prepared detailing the nature of the secondary professional co-operative.

Contracting

Individual funds obtain information in the preparatory year. This is used to negotiate contracts with providers for individual contracts, having obtained information from providers on services available.

Quality and clinical issues

These will be determined by doctors only and guidelines drawn up for the discussion and approval of funds before negotiation takes place. Patients will have an input via questionnaires used to audit the provision of care by providers.

The final negotiating team will consist of the consortium manager, area managers and board representatives where appropriate.

There are now many consortia in existence, most of the larger ones being based on the multifund structure. They have already started to deliver the benefits alluded to earlier in the chapter, and will no doubt play an increasingly important role in the commissioning of care. Within the new style health service, consortia will become a crucial factor in the maintenance and development of the ideals of the NHS. Only when all practices are covered by consortia or legislation is introduced giving statutory rights to non-fundholding groups, will the ideal of equity of care be preserved.

13

A Consortium Approach

Ian Walker

Since the inception of fundholding it has been clear that a consortium - style approach, not only to contracting, but to work related to fundholding in general, has several advantages. A formal consortium is not required to accrue benefits, an informal grouping of localized practices with similar intentions is sufficient.

Firstly, it has the advantage of increased buyer power and influence over provider units - the level of activity contracted for will 'impress' the unit management, and dealing with one 'group' rather than three or four different practices makes their management task more straightforward.

Secondly, the sharing of good practice and innovative ideas prevents each practice attempting to 'reinvent the wheel' and can speed problem solving when the same or similar problems have been encountered before.

Thirdly, and possibly the most important advantage for the fund manager is the security of having someone close at hand to offer assistance and encouragement.

There are three major areas that need to be concentrated on for success in the first year of taking on a fund.

1. Identifying the initial allocation of funding and associated activity to preferred provider units.

2. Specifying priority quality requirements for contract negotiation.

3. Systems/information management to facilitate budget management and contract monitoring.

The initial decision on the proportion of funds to be allocated to provider units has tended to be based on recent experience with the practices' local units. To date, where the practice has reasonable access to services and good communication with local consultants approximately 80% of total activity and funding has been committed at the negotiation table. Where access to the hospital for routine appointments and non-urgent procedures is poor and there are unacceptably long waiting times less has been committed initially.

Activity data

Critical to this allocation of funds has been the price per fund-holding item and a definite understanding by both parties involved as to what this price includes. A detailed analysis of the overall level of the budget together with the pricing structure is essential to understand the level of activity which can be bought during the financial year. A complicating factor in the activity planning for the first wave was the announcement of the inclusion of the chronic out-patient attender in addition to new referrals.

Where practices have collected new referrals in their preparatory year data collection, an estimate of total attendances of their patients at all providers has been difficult; and where they have collected out-patient attendance letters this has generally been too low due to consultants not sending a letter after every out-patient attendance. Further complications arise if hospital data are used as most hospital outpatient information systems are crude and unable to distinguish patients between practices. A crude 'best guess' estimate is available from hospitals. Most specialties can provide an overall ratio of total follow-up appointments to new referrals for GPs using the unit. This ratio can be used by the practice as a starting point for calculating total out-patient activity and cost. Ultimately the difficulties in approximating the current years total out-patient costs can be simplified if the provider unit will agree to a price per new referral which is inclusive of all follow up visits relevant to that referral plus all chronic attenders to that specialty from the practice. If this is done the practice has no 'threat' of the unknown extra costs of chronic out-patient attenders and the unit is relieved of the problem of identifying each out-patient episode and invoicing for them; they invoice per new referral only. It is important to establish exactly what is included in a price quoted by a provider unit:

- For out-patients, is it per referral (inclusive of all follow-ups for that patient), or per attendance? Does the price include all tests, investigations and fundholding procedures undertaken as a direct result of the out-patient assessment or follow-up appointment, or are they billed separately?

- What does the in-patient/day-case procedure price include? Is it inclusive of tests and investigations carried out during the admission and does it include any out-patient assessments or follow-ups associated with the procedure carried out?

It is important to be entirely clear about what is included in a price and what is to be billed for separately. This needs to be explicit in the contract to avoid surprises and disputes during the year.

Contract negotiation

The second area of major work has been contract negotiation, so far, the most time consuming and frustrating. While individual practices have had very clear ideas on important quality related issues – discharge information, waiting times for out-patient appointments and in-patient admissions; many weeks of meetings with and telephone calls to, hospital units have been spent explaining the fundholding concept and how it differs from the district purchaser/provider unit relationship to hospitals with little experience of fundholding practices.

One of the principal differences from this relationship is that fundholding practices can be much more specific in detailing proposed activity and quality perspectives, thereby directly representing their patient population. District purchasers can only represent patients indirectly and thus need to be much more general in the specification and activity detail. Other major areas of difference are:

- fundholding practices are much more flexible in adapting to possible alternative providers

- information requirements of the fundholding budget monitoring system are more detailed than district purchasers, indeed the fundholding software is probably three years in advance of the system capabilities of both providers and district purchasers.

The most effective way of forcing the pace in contract negotiations has been to detail the requirements of practices in activity, quality specification information and invoicing requirements through a fundholding specific contract outline produced by the fundholding practices. Although an easier option, using the contracts produced between district purchasers and providers allows for little differentiation and future flexibility and proves costly for practices later in the year, particularly in the area of detailed contract monitoring. Specific fundholder contracts force hospital managers and consultants to respond to requirements in detail which facilitates more productive negotiations.

There have been a few cases where contracts have been agreed and it has subsequently been discovered that hospital managers have not read them fully and are now realizing the consequences. More seriously some hospital consultants have been unaware of them or of the fundholding concept. It is very important that fundholding GPs communicate directly with consultants they know well, as this 'understanding' filters through the hospital consultants, albeit slowly. Without the agreement of those who deliver the service, contracts are not worth the paper they are written on!

It is important not to commit everything initially. If the provider unit is guaranteed all of a practice's funding up front in, say, a block contract there is very little incentive for them to improve services. Agreeing to commit further funding at the half year point if the unit is delivering the service as negotiated in the contract is a much better motivator for change and improvement.

Generally the author has overseen negotiated contracts which are a hybrid of cost and volume and cost per case. Indicative volumes are given but payment is based on actual provision of care and invoiced in arrears. If an agreement is reached to provide monthly payments up front as a prepayment, quarterly reviews are used to review future payments according to actual activity reported in the previous quarter. In this way the provider unit cannot become complacent about the contract.

Monitoring

The third area of activity is that of systems and information management to facilitate budget and contract monitoring.

An important concept to grasp is that the fundholding financial system is run on the accounting concept of accruals. Simply, this means that the expenditure for fundholding activity is accounted for when it is known to have taken place, eg from a discharge letter, irrespective of the practice receiving an invoice. This leads to the fundholding practice reporting more expenditure than hospitals have been able to invoice for, and the accrued expenditure appearing to vanish in the eyes of provider units. It is important to reconcile these differences with hospital finance departments during the year to allow them to plan ahead with the most accurate financial information.

The information requirements of both parties need to be specified exactly in the contracts and a detailed understanding needs to be fostered between the people operating the respective systems. Hospital information managers benefit from seeing the fundholding software in operation and understanding why a contract number is required, what a referral number generated for each patient is and the importance of waiting list information and detailed patient activity and costs for contract and budget monitoring.

Each practice needs to establish a system to monitor the performance of the provider unit against the contract. Some sort of exception reporting system, similar in principle to the referral exception report on the fundholding software, needs to be devised to bring the relevant facts and data to the attention of all parties concerned. The main areas of contract compliance monitoring used in the author's region are waiting times and discharge information. It is important to have a clear understanding and commitment to operate sanctions or penalties when hospitals fail to meet agreed standards. Without them, contracts have little impact when standards fall. One of the easiest ways to operate is to ensure that no payment is made without a formal clinical letter from the clinician treating the patient. Another very topical issue is the matter of hospital prescribing. Where the agreed minimal prescribing protocols are not met and the cost of prescribing falls to the practice, a reduced payment (or no payment) can be made for that particular treatment.

Conclusion

It is important that whoever is responsible for managing the three major areas of activity described above understands the interactions between the interested groups: GPs, provider units, district purchasers, FHSAs, RHAs and private providers, and actively communicates and balances the different expectations of each party. It is extremely important that fundholders within each area communicate with each other to share ideas, concerns and possibly purchasing power to avoid being isolated and potentially vulnerable to a well-prepared provider unit negotiating team.

14

The Beginner's Guide to the Community Health Services Budget

Peter Smith and Mercedes Kelly-Madden

In July 1992 the National Health Services Management Executive published the Yellow Book (white in Scotland) which detailed the extension of the fundholding scheme to cover Community Health Services. In December of the same year, a useful supplementary guidance paper was issued covering the Children Act 1989 and giving further clarification on inclusions and exclusions.

The Community Health Services Budget should not be confused with the Community Care Act provisions, which also came into force from 1 April 1993. These covered the rationalization of other community services and the transfer of responsibility for many of them to the Social Services Department (SSD). In addition an integrated approach to care in the home was developed, combining the skills of district nurses and home care assistants. Readers in Northern Ireland should note that in 1993 there were no plans to introduce either the Community Health Services element to the budget or the Community Care Act.

The inclusion of the Community Health Services budget in the fundholding scheme has produced an unnecessary level of angst amongst existing and prospective fundholders. The rather sketchy knowledge of most GPs of the scope of services and skills available in the community has left many rather bewildered about what is required of them. This problem has been compounded by the lack of useful information available from local providers. The reaction of many fundholders has therefore been to opt for the status quo rather than using the opportunity to make changes. This chapter gives an aerial view of the subject, to assist you in planning your own foray into this hitherto apparently uncharted territory.

We hope that you will then feel confident enough to delve

into the existing literature. The Yellow Book itself is essential reading, covering contracts and quality issues, giving detailed results of a recent study of the workload of a group of community nurses and even including specimen contracts. Refined versions of these are given in the supplementary guidance document, which also offers sensible advice on issues to be negotiated in contracts. Having considered all these aspects, funds can still decide to go for the easy way out and opt for fixed-price non-attributable contracts.

Fixed-price non-attributable contracts

Detailed information about community health services is lacking in most localities. Fixed-price non-attributable contracts were therefore introduced to allow fundholders to fulfil their obligation to contract for services even when information was sketchy. The price is not related to volume of referrals or activity, with a fixed payment made monthly over the period of the contract. The advantage of this is that no referrals need to be recorded in the fundholding software – costs and referrals are therefore not attributable to individual patients. This differs from block contracts, where individual patients incur specific notional costs.

It was recognized that this type of contract allowed providers and purchasers to take stock before making changes. Therefore in the first year that this element was introduced into the scheme (ie from April 1993) all negotiations for community nursing were limited to non-attributable contracts. Obviously, as information gathering improves (as it must if fundholding is to be of any use at all in these areas), more funds will feel happy making their own quality stipulations and juggling with skill mixes.

Since there is no way of assessing the cost of treatment of an individual patient, the £5,000 limit does not apply to non-attributable contracts. It does apply, however, if other types of contract are made for community health services.

Protocols

Most of the services covered by the community health services element of the budget will continue to receive referrals from non-GPs for which the fundholder is liable. A significant element of expenditure will therefore be outside the GPs' control, and it will be essential in all these areas to develop referral protocols to ensure that inappropriate referrals are kept to a minimum. As community health services effectively undergo audit through the fundholding system, there is no doubt that such guidelines will be come much more refined and play an increasingly important role in defining and developing the scope of activities of community health professionals.

Services covered

- District nurses ⎫
- Health visitors ⎬ Community nursing services
- Chiropody (except self-referrals).
- Dietetics.
- All community and out-patient mental health services.
- Mental health counselling.
- Health services for people with a learning disability.
- Referrals made by health visitors, district nurses and community mental handicap nurses.
- Management costs.

Services still excluded

- School medical services.
- Community medical services.
- Orthoptics.

Examples follow of details to be considered when negotiating community contracts.

Community nursing services

This element of the budget includes district nurses, health visitors and aids and appliances. It does not include specialist nurses such as terminal and stoma care – these will remain the responsibility of the DHA. Fortunately it is recommended that equipment, aids and appliances used by the community nursing services should be included under the overheads part of the budget and distributed proportionately; it will not be necessary to track down every item. Fundholders will be obliged to contract only with NHS providers for these services and will not be able to employ them directly or contract with private providers. They will, however, be able to use a different NHS provider.

Where fundholders make changes in the existing provision, for instance by reducing the grading of nurses provided, they will be legally responsible for any problems that may arise as a result of having less qualified staff.

With limited nurse prescribing in place from October 1993, protocols for treatment will have to be established at an early stage to ensure that unnecessary conflicts do not arise.

A rather interesting quirk of the system is that community nursing for a GP's private patients will be paid for by the DHA, because they are still entitled to the NHS service but are not covered by the GP's fund.

The following points need to be considered in contracts for community nursing services (much of this information has been abstracted from government publications).

1: What activities does the service cover now?

What are the Core Services and what are the Specialist Areas (eg Terminal Care Nursing)?

2: What staff are currently in place?

Is the current grade mix appropriate to deliver the level and range of services required and what scope is there to adjust this? What arrangements are in place for the training and development of staff including individual performance review?

3: Quality issues

What are the existing standards of delivery of the service (eg times to first contact after receipt of referral, levels of contact with children under five and expectant mothers, immunization, vaccination and child health surveillance)? What will be done to ensure the effective use of resources (eg protocols for referrals, arrangements for reporting on inappropriate referrals and grade mix)?

4: Continuity of care

How is continuity of care to be ensured (eg named community nurse responsible for patient's care, transfer of patient records)?

5: Access to services

How is the availability of services determined, including assessment of patients' needs? Are interpreters available and are leaflets available in ethnic minority languages where applicable?

6: Service venues

Where are services delivered (eg patients' homes, surgeries, health centres etc)?

7: Primary health care team responsibilities

These will probably be practice specific.

8: Health promotion and health education policies

These will differ from practice to practice, but will need to be agreed with community nurses to ensure continuity of advice.

9: Monitoring

How are outcomes measured? Are patient satisfaction surveys carried out? What contract monitoring and reporting arrangements are in place and how often will reports be available?

10: Price

Costs should include no planned cross-subsidization to benefit or disadvantage the fundholder. What is the frequency of payment? Are changes to the grade mix to be made during the year?

11: Variation of service levels

Could the service be expanded?

12: Cross-boundary agreements

Will an additional contract be necessary for patients living outside the district boundary? This is a crucial consideration – just a few families in a neighbouring community unit area can make a significant difference to the budget.

Chiropody

Funding for this area (as for dietetics) will be based on previous level of NHS referrals. Until other provisions are made, this will unfortunately mean that, unless funds are vired from another element of the budget, areas with poor NHS provision of these services will remain under-provided. Fundholders may employ these professionals if they wish, either by using an element of their staff budget allocated for this purpose by the FHSA, or by viring from other areas. Since patients referred to chiropodists may require treatment for many years, this will need to be taken into account when making contracts. The following points need to be considered in contacts for chiropody.

1: Range of services

Does the existing service offer preventive, palliative and corrective care (eg does it include maintaining tissue viability, work under local anaesthetic, minor ops procedures, orthotic work, domiciliary visits to the housebound as well as basic footcare)? Would chiropodists be able to attend practice diabetic clinics?

2: Staffing

Are staff appropriately trained with a range of skills available? Are foot-care assistants employed? Is regular training available and are staff subject to clinical and managerial review?

3: Continuity of care

Will a named chiropodist be responsible for an individual patient? Are protocols in place to cover referrals to consultant medical staff?

4: Clinical need

Is a treatment plan with proposed outcomes prepared? Does the range of services include maintenance, palliative care and short-term treatment? How are clinical records maintained? How are outcomes measured, both in short-term and long-term care? Are resources available at present to treat patients as often as is clinically necessary? Are patients advised on self-help and preventive measures?

5: Access

How soon are patients seen after referral? How are patients referred and seen in an emergency? What are average waiting times for treatment? Are patients seen within half an hour of their appointment time? How are non-attenders dealt with?

6: Venues

Can services be provided at GP surgeries, health centres, residential homes and on a domiciliary basis?

7: Health & Safety

Is the treatment venue used equipped with an electro-hydraulic chair or couch, an autoclave, at least two sets of instruments and a nail drill with dust extractor?

8: Information

What monitoring information will be provided and how often? How often will meetings take place to discuss performance compared to contract?

9: Price

Prices must be based on full cost with no cross-subsidization. A range of prices should be offered covering foot-care assistant work, operative procedures, orthotics and domiciliary visits.

10: Contracts

A range of contracts should be offered, including tailored packages including specialist services. Will the contract cover patients living outside the area?

11: Development of service

Could the following additional services be provided: podiatric surgery, modifications to patients' footwear, involvement in GP over-75 assessments and involvement in diabetic miniclinics?

12: Ethnic minorities

Is information available to cover the ethnic minorities that exist within the area?

All community and out-patient mental health services

Acute psychiatric referrals, psychiatric in-patient treatment and day care services are specifically excluded from the budget. However, if a practice has an attached CPN at present, these services will be charged to the practice. This section does not include self referrals (eg to drug addiction clinics and drop-in centres). These have been excluded in order to safeguard entry to care for those patients who might not wish to attend a GP clinic.

Child guidance and child psychiatry referrals *are* included.

Mental health counselling

Since funding for this section will be based on previous NHS activity and since the NHS provides very little in the way of counselling, the Yellow Book concedes that the amount that individual funds will receive will be minimal, unless they already employ a counsellor.

Health services for people with a learning disability

Some confusion has arisen over the meaning of the term 'people with a learning disability'. This term is politically correct, but synonymous with the older term 'mental handicap'. (Even the Yellow Book lapses into use of the old term in its Contents page). The Supplementary document issued in December 1992 recommended that non-attributable fixed-price contracts should be made to cover this element. It rather obliquely refers to this as a 'contracting easement'. Until accurate figures are available, non-attributable contracts would seem to be the best option. Partly because many providers are finding it difficult to collect sufficient data, and secondly because although these services are not necessarily requested by GPs, the intention is that all such referrals will be funded. Clearly, an important issue for the future will be preparation of protocols for acceptance of referrals and informing the fund. This process will have to be refined to obtain useful information before any other sort of contract can be made, in order to obtain accurate information.

This section does not include services provided within schools for children with learning disabilities.

The future of the community health services budget

The most important issues that will decide the success or failure of this element of the scheme are as follows.

1: Information technology

Unless more efficient systems are developed to reduce the amount of time taken collecting the information necessary to establish patient volumes and activity, many fundholders are likely to continue to opt for the non-attributable type of contract, since information will remain inaccurate. Most current systems waste too much of the professional's valuable time providing information for contractors.

2: Funding

Throughout the documents referred to above, there are references to the lack of existing NHS services, eg covering chiropody and counselling. Since budgets will be based on existing use, there will be little scope for dramatically improving these services unless extra funding is made available to cover the unmet need as it is revealed.

3: Understanding

There is no doubt that GPs will have to develop a greater understanding of the role of the health professionals mentioned in the legislation if they are to be able to enter into contract negotiation sensibly.

If these areas are addressed, the inclusion of community health services could well prove to be crucial to the further development of community care.

Further reading

The Yellow Book (July 1992) *Guidance on the extension of the hospital and community health, services elements of the GP fundholding scheme from 1 April 1993*. NHS Management Executive. Document Reference No.: EL(92)48.

Supplementary Guidance (December 1992) *The extension of the hospital and community health services elements of the*

GP fundholding scheme from 1 April 1993 – supplementary guidance' NHS Management Executive. Document Reference No.: HSG(92)5.

Both these documents may be obtained from RHAs, and from:

The DoH Store
Health Publications Unit
No. 2 Site
Manchester Road
Heywood
Lancashire OL10 2 PZ.

In cases of difficulty only, contact Anne Mather at the Department of Health on 071 972 8176.

To date, *'Fundholding'* magazine (Haymarket Publications) has published several useful articles giving further suggestions on the different areas of the community health, services budget, in particular community nursing (Vol 1, No. 18, 7 September 1992); chiropody (Vol 1, No. 19, 21 September 1992); and dietetics (Vol. 1, No. 20, 7 October 1992)

15

Prescribing Choices

Barry Strickland-Hodge

Over the past few years, prescribing choices in general practice appear to have been restricted. The limited list cut a number of preparations that had been widely used by GPs and this number is currently being extended. In 1988, Prescribing Analysis and Cost (PACT) was launched by the Prescription Pricing Authority (PPA), from which GPs could identify the preparations they had prescribed and the associated costs. Since then, the thrust has been a downward pressure on cost, although the current term used is a 'downward pressure on waste.'

PACT is being adapted to give improved information; fundholding continues to offer GPs the opportunity to manage their own services; there is encouragement to prescribe generically and to introduce practice formularies. All these changes have been outlined in the various White Papers over the past six years.

Working for patients

The major reforms were outlined in the White Papers *Working for Patients* and *Caring for People*. In these documents, the indicative prescribing scheme, fundholding, hospital trusts and community care were each described and discussed. The Government ideas as outlined in the White Papers subsequently became law as the NHS and Community Care Act 1990.

Spending in the first two years of the schemes

Apart from individual practices, FHSAs generally have stayed reasonably well within the amounts set. The largest amounts of overspending was by those FHSAs who set the first amounts based on historic spending plus 13.5% and some uplifts. One FHSA which overspent by less than 1% stated that it gave an overall increase on the historic 1989/90 spending of almost 30%. The current method of calculating the following year's annual out-turn from part of the current year is more accurate than the former method. However, sensitivity as to the correct factors to apply is essential.

Why should practices overspend?

There have been many reasons cited for the overspending. One is that spending was incorrectly formulated, the first year being heralded as a learning year. Others suggest that there was as much as a 100% increase in the amount of hospital-shifted prescribing. The cost of these hospital initiated items was transferred or dumped onto general practice at a time of stringent cost containment in the hospital sector. Practices are continuing to accept prescribing responsibility for an increased number of drugs that traditionally would be consultant-managed. This could lead to greater patient convenience and more primary care involvement, as long as the GP is fully involved in the treatment and is not called upon only to sign the prescriptions.

Changes in the practice have been cited as another important factor in the apparent increase in prescribing costs. Increasing numbers of patients, practices remaining open for longer hours and offering new services, and thus attracting more patients, can all lead to higher costs. Changes that occurred after the historic spending was calculated can obviously lead to overspending if the FHSAs are not informed and action taken on the amount offered.

Health promotion clinics have been encouraged, but when these come out in favour of specific treatment such as for hyperlipidaemia, then costs will inevitably rise. In the long term these clinics will save the NHS money. Uplifts need to reflect this now. During recessions, such as the current one, it is acknowledged that the number of patients visiting a doctor increases. This can be because of more patient availability during the day and because problems that may have been accepted as self-limiting are now brought to the attention of the doctor. The script volume is increasing more than had been anticipated. The implementation of the Community Care Act also has the potential to cause a further increase in the script volume of general practice.

The prescribing process

If we are looking at a downward pressure on waste rather than merely looking at cost, then over-prescribing is an important issue. Fundholders in particular should spend time considering their prescribing, not with the view of changing from one product to another, but generally deciding if a product is really necessary in each case. There are a number of complex pressures placed upon the general practitioner during a consultation and cultural, social, patient and organizational factors can influence the course of drug prescribing.

There are many reasons why a GP prescribes. For example, research carried out in the 1970s indicated that doctor expectation of a patient's expectation of a prescription was higher than the patient's original expectation. This resulted in over-prescribing in some cases. There have been a number of research papers looking at the reasons why a GP writes a prescription:

- to fulfil patient expectations
- because there is no time to do anything else
- to deal with uncertainty
- to legitimize the patient in the sick role
- to end the consultation
- to comply with the wishes of another doctor

- to impress or mystify the patient
- because of sheer habit
- to maintain contact with the patient
- to avoid doing something else
- to satisfy an urge to give.

Often the prescription is the most convenient way of telling a patient that they have not wasted the doctor's or their own time; they have a recognized condition, it can be treated, and the consultation is now over.

Drug cost awareness

PACT, the Indicative Prescribing Scheme and fundholding have all been created to increase awareness of the cost of drugs. *Working for Patients* not only mentions the various schemes which are now in operation, it also encourages the creation of practice formularies. The White Paper suggests that these should be practice-based and voluntary.

No one would deny that improvements could be made in prescribing. There is over-prescribing, unnecessary and costly prescribing. Cost, however, is only one aspect of any therapeutic decision. There is little or no evidence that high cost is necessarily related to bad prescribing any more than low cost is necessarily related to good prescribing. It is important to distinguish the various factors which make up a rational decision in choosing a product for a specific patient, and then see where cost fits.

Rational prescribing

This has been the subject of a number of papers over the last 20 years when Peter Parish first published criteria for rational prescribing. These criteria have formed the core of papers since then. However, it is important to take away the research aspect of rational prescribing and look more at what it means to individual practitioners and patients. Does it have to mean cheap prescribing? Must there be a link between outcome of treatment and product choice? Does it mean that we need to put cost back into context, and make outcome and patient satisfaction the key elements? Is a prescription always necessary?

Prescribing is a response to a complex set of criteria. Making a rational choice involves an ever-increasing set of factors. Once a prescription is deemed to be necessary (taking into account patient expectation and risk benefit analysis), the prescriber must consider each individual patient and select an appropriate product in an appropriate dosage and form. This product must be effective and safe at the selected dose. Finally cost should be considered. In other words, the four key elements are:

- necessity
- effectiveness
- safety
- cost.

GPs consider that cost is an element in rational prescribing and that excessive prescribing may be due to a realization that the placebo effect is important. In a recent survey, 40% of GPs considered that there was a place for placebo drugs in rational prescribing. Has the limited list meant that more potent and expensive products are now being used as placebos?

Rational prescribing should start with the patient and could follow the criteria: Necessary to prescribe product; Outcome of the treatment acceptable; Safe at these dose levels?; Effective at this dose and for the duration given; Generic if available; Acceptable to the patient in this form; Economic.

Prescribing is not simple. Rational prescribing is even more complex. It is not necessarily cheap and must take account of the patient and the outcome of treatment. Costs need to be placed into context. Rational prescribing is patient orientated not cost orientated. Taking patient acceptability into account should be the aim of all prescribers.

Generic prescribing

Switching from a branded product to a generic 'equivalent' is not so simple when there are so many different preparations which the patient may be given. These often differ in colour, size, and shape from the original and from each other.

There are times when a generic drug will be unacceptable to a certain patient. The shape, the size and the colour may all cause unsatisfactory compliance.

Cost-effective prescribing with generic drugs

There are certain products which have run through their patent life and have a satisfactory generic equivalent which are both cost-effective and rational to prescribe. Where there is a large difference in price between the branded and non-branded products, the generic drug should be considered whenever possible taking patient compliance into account. A 'best-buys list' should be prepared for GPs.

Concentrating on generic drugs as a whole, however, takes away the impact which could be obtained by careful attention to the detail of PACT. The local community pharmacist can help here. It also ignores the input of the pharmaceutical industry in innovative research. Branded products have a major place in general practice therapy. Innovations are essential, and industry and medical information departments can bring about a more sophisticated system of information delivery. With changes in patent protection it is hoped that companies will be given a reasonable length of time during which to recoup research and staff costs and to continue further research.

There are two main areas of continuing concern among GPs: safety (including equivalency and bio-availability), and patient confusion.

With regard to safety, there are a small number of preparations where continued care is essential and where patient continuation on a particular brand *or* on the generic should be maintained. If a patient is stabilized on one form, change can have clinical implications for the patients.

Patient confusion, particularly concerning special formulations and capsules, is a common problem. Patients given a prescription for temazepam are faced with an array of different-coloured capsules. Patients used to branded inhalers in a particular coloured box may be confused when given a generic alternative. Apart from colour, taste may differ. Company back-up for patients and doctors may also be a consideration. Packaging may be used by patients to aid compliance (eg calendar packs); these will be different in generic equivalents. Generic drugs are often cheaper (though certainly not always), and patient acceptability should be taken into account when making a final decision.

Formularies

In an atmosphere of cost-containment and a downward pressure on waste, formularies are an obvious discussion point among fundholders. The White Paper, *Working for Patients* points out the relevance of formularies, and *Improving Prescribing* says that they should be voluntary and practice-based. Only in this latter form can they fulfil the potential of a learning experience. Thinking about prescribing and choosing products to match situations and individuals can be beneficial to both doctor and patient.

Existing national and local formularies

Formularies should not be seen as restrictive lists. They do not use only generic products and they do not cover all events. Some suggest that the formulary should be acceptable in 85% of patient consultations. Others say a more realistic figure is 75%. Most writers do say that the most important aspect of any written formulary is that it should be updated regularly. There is a place for innovative preparations when there is enough information on which to make a decision.

There are a number of formularies which have been published and which can be used as guides: eg the 1993 Northern Ireland Royal College formulary, the 1992 Lothian formulary and the Basic Formulary for General Practice. Looking at the products included can help the selection.

PACT Level 3 can be used as a starting point for discussions with colleagues, medical or pharmaceutical advisers and pharmacists. Using products with which both the patients and the doctors are experienced will lead to a better adherence to the list and a simpler transition.

The hospital formulary has a place in aspects of prescribing particularly where GPs consider there is a 'high risk' associated with the drug group or the disease state. In all other cases, it is recommended that the GP creates his or her own formulary to include the preparations the practice feels most sure of and which patients find acceptable, taking dosage forms and effectiveness into account.

When prescribing in areas of 'high risk', it is likely that a GP will either refer the patient to a consultant in a hospital or make a decision on the best information available.

The effect of formularies

Not everyone believes that formularies will lower costs or improve care. In economic terms, formularies have yet to be fully appraised. The other approach is for a policy decision in particular therapeutic areas. This means deciding on the type approach rather than concentrating on specific product lists.·

Perhaps determining the balance between the use of different preparations in the same therapeutic area, rather than concentrating simply on cost, may turn out to be the key factor for cost containment.

There is no national selection policy for new drugs or established products for the formulary. Trusts and major hospitals have their own. There may be a common core of preparations, with two or three alternatives.

General practice core prescribing list

General practitioners should be encouraged to make their own formularies and, when most are formed, perhaps 25% of the preparations could be used to make up a core formulary. This could be taken to the providers in the hospital to look at the differences between their formulary and the GP's. The provider units should then tie in with this core GP list after first differentiating between hospital-only products and others.

The out-patient department deals with chronic illnesses, so two formularies may be necessary: one for discharge and one for out-patients. For the remaining 75% of preparations, some will be hospital-only or will always be initiated by the hospital. When the GP is expected to continue the treatment in the community, shared care notes on the chosen products should be prepared for each GP. The problem of differential pricing may be overcome with the merging of the DHAs and FHSAs, which could lead to a joint approach to purchasing, leading to contracts for the most appropriate products taking the core formulary and the cost to the community into account.

The idea of a district-wide local prescribing policy was voiced in the *Drug and Therapeutics Bulletin* in 1990, on the grounds that it would lead to more rational prescribing and thus more effective treatment. On entering and leaving hospital, patients could be maintained on the same products being used in the community. If the policy was based on a selected list or formulary, the doctors and other staff could become familiar with these, leading to less confusion. Obviously before such a policy could be constructed, there would have to be agreement between all parties. Hospital consultants should accept the input from GPs and, as mentioned above, primary care practitioners should lead the way. Any list must be flexible enough to admit new preparations and developments. The *Drug and Therapeutics Bulletin* suggests that local drugs and therapeutics committees should invite appropriate local specialists and GPs, provider's pharmaceutical officers, FHSA medical and pharmaceutical advisers and community pharmacists to meetings to discuss relevant parts of the proposed policy. Drafts should be circulated to all GPs for comment. Fundholding contracts could be the starting point.

Conclusion

Prescribing choices remain with general practitioners. As we near the year 2000, primary care will assume a more central role in health care. GP prescribing methods need to be rationalized so that they can be used as the model for prescribing for hospital out-patients. A core general practice list is recommended and, through a local prescribing policy, this should be incorporated into the hospital formulary.

Rational prescribing should begin and end with the patient. Cost must be put back into context and rational prescribing should lead the way.

The creation of practice formularies is a good educational exercise. However, they are voluntary and should be practice-based for the majority of problems encountered in general practice. Products in hospital should be selected for therapeutic reasons only, not cost to the hospital. If diagnosis leads to a selection of products known to be cheaper in the hospital than in the community, the consultant or pharmacy should either inform the patient that this is for an acute attack of the problem, and that new therapy from the GP may differ, or recommend that the patient visits the GP for treatment, after they have informed the GP of the choices recommended.

Hospital-shifted prescribing remains a major issue in general practice. If it is to continue, changes are essential. The major problems centre on the liability of prescribing. If this is retained by the consultant, and only cost is to be transferred, then some of the irritation currently felt could be alleviated. Contracts to account for the costs of treatments managed by the hospital provider (including the cost of drugs) should be drawn up by fundholders. Rational prescribing is not necessarily cheap and the products used are not necessarily generic. Primary care needs to provide a cohesive service to patients. All professionals need to become involved if we are to maintain a healthy health service. The prescribing choice must return to the hands of the primary care specialists, and stay there.

16

Locality Commissioning: A Partnership with Fundholding

Andrew Burnett

The core element of GP fundholding is the purchasing of care for the people registered in the fundholding practice. While a GP fundholder may use the contracting process to influence the care supplied by providers for other non-fundholding practices, the commissioning of care for the majority is still done by District Health Authorities and Social Services departments. This chapter looks at some of the issues involved in enabling wider input into the commissioning process, and how fundholders and non-fundholders can achieve greater influence and health gain for the people they care for by working together.

Definitions

In this chapter, 'commissioning' refers to the determination of service requirements. 'Purchasing' is the negotiation for, and buying of, services so defined. Commissioners and purchasers are not necessarily the same people or even in the same organization.

Partnerships in care: separation or co-operation?

The purchaser–provider split need not be schismatic. It creates the potential for working partnerships between two groups who share a common ultimate aim – improving people's health – but who come to it from different directions. A differentiation between those who commission and/or purchase care and those who provide it helps to clarify roles, creates a platform for needs-based care provision and generates a creative tension which drives innovation.

The NHS reforms have emphasized the unique position of the general practitioner: that of being a direct provider of health care and also a gatekeeper, by referral, to care provided by others in the NHS and elsewhere. In consequence, the GP determines the use of a majority of resources of the Health Service.

These reforms have also led to some District Health Authorities amalgamating and either merging completely or working in close relationship with Family Health Services Authorities in Commissioning Agencies. Some Commissioning Agencies also commission care jointly with Social Services departments. Most such agencies will become Health Authorities (replacing districts) in the next 1–3 years.

The local team

The concept that service provision should be defined by assessing needs (and subsequently prioritizing them) raises questions about the mechanisms for developing a strategy for care.

The NHS reforms have created two foci for the purchase of care: the commissioning agency/Health Authority and the GP fundholder. *See* Figure 16.1.

What of the non-fundholding GP? Throughout the country, systems are evolving to enable the co-ordinated input of others into purchasing decisions, thus creating a purchasing 'spectrum'.

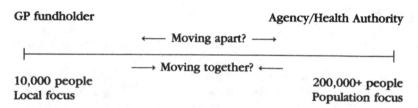

Figure 16.1.

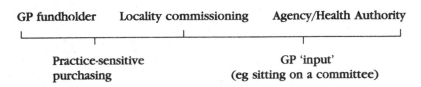

Figure 16.2.

Clearly, overall care strategy must be directed by a 'top-down', epidemiologically based, assessment of need and subsequent prioritization will take account of both this and resource availability.

The Health of the Nation provides a lead, but Regional, District and Family Health Services Authorities will have subsidiary strategies to add. However, such a top-down approach inevitably lacks sensitivity to local areas, where atypical but significant variations in need and resources can exist.

Thus the development of a 'bottom-up' approach is also required. Those who work in the community are best placed to act as well informed advocates of service users. The primary care team, which will include the Social Services Department, if aligned to the same service users is the linchpin of local needs assessment and service provision. *See* Figure 16.3.

Localities

To provide a local focus to enable the commissioning and purchasing of care, many parts of the country are developing 'localities', which may be based on:

- a 'natural community', eg a town or a large estate within an urban area
- a geographical area, eg an area demarcated by natural and man-made boundaries – rivers, roads, etc
- an administration area, eg borough council areas, electoral wards
- a functional unit, eg a GP practice catchment population or aggregations of these.

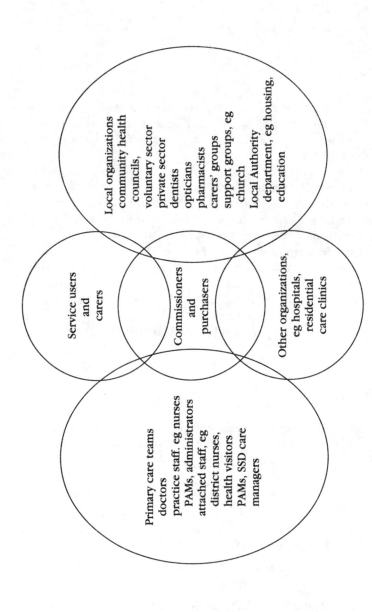

Figure 16.3: Locality commissioning creates a collaborative structure which aligns the users of services with those who commission purchase and provide them.

There is not yet a tested model which is either complete or transportable to other areas. Inevitably, there is an evolutionary approach in the development of localities and their function.

Purchaser/provider co-operation

This involves:

- mechanisms for GPs to agree with each other and with medical, nursing and other colleagues about how best to identify needs and allocate resources to provide high-quality care over a broad range and with value for money
- equitable distribution of resources
- efficiency of management with reduction of overheads
- linkage of GP fundholding and GP non-fundholding schemes to improve equity and promote examples of good practice
- minimization of fragmentation for Health Authorities, NHS trusts, GP fundholders and GP non-fundholders.

Ideally it will encompass:

- all GP practices
- all (other) providers, including the local authority Social Services department
- all commissioners and purchasers of care, including the Local Authority Social Services department.

Important issues for enhanced care include:

- professional accountability, which must not be diluted
- co-ordinated teamworking and team identity, which can be achieved through having common service users
- improved communication, through common task-sharing
- joint assessment, joint management and thereby joint responsibility

- greater satisfaction for commissioners, purchasers, providers and service users.

Locality commissioning

Aided by information supplied through commissioning agencies, the GP non-fundholder can be put in a similar position to that of the GP fundholder to formulate local health care plans augmented with the benefit of local knowledge.

Basing localities on GP practice populations creates congruency between GP fundholders and GP non-fundholders, and generates synergy between them.

Suitable aggregations of GP practice-registered populations, and appropriate management of those in the 'localities' thereby created, can permit the commissioning of care with a locally based perspective – a bottom-up approach. This is allied to a top-down approach and thereby blends local circumstances with overall strategy. Such 'locality commissioning' leads to the empowerment of users, carers and those who serve them.

- If those working in the community are not empowered, managers cannot enable schemes to work.

- If those working in the community are empowered, there is local ownership and managers are also empowered, because schemes can then work.

The key issues for successful locality working are summarized in Figure 16.4.

Teamwork between practices and their staff, both employed and attached, and liaison with providers and commissioning agencies, enables rational and locally sensitive commissioning of care: sensitive to higher 'strategy', local needs and local resources. It encourages holistic rather than separatist health and social care-management of people, awareness of carers' needs, knowledge of service duplication by different providers, knowledge of lack of service provision by any provider and easier identification of inefficient, ineffective and baroque service provision mechanisms. It can thereby increase health gain and value for money.

Planning objectives

- Shared agenda between authorities, commissioners, purchasers, providers and service users.
- Identification of needs, resources and priorities.
- Flexible responsiveness to identified needs.
- Equitable service provision.
- Consistency of high standards.

Management objectives

- Seamless care provision
  - multidisciplinary working
  - functional co-terminosity.
- Blending top-down with bottom-up.
- Accountability.
- Value for money.

Support objectives

- Clear joint policies.
- Empowerment of managers, providers and consumers.
- Realistic incentives for change.

Outcome objectives

- Increased health gain.
- Improved responsiveness.
- Better accessibility to care.
- Effective and efficient use of resources.

Figure 16.4: *Locality working*. Key issues for successful working, from which locality commissioning can flow.

Commissioning by a locality in this way, from the bottom-up, draws together the service user, primary care teams and commissioning authorities.

The size of a locality, varying perhaps between 100,000 and 180,000, but critically the supporting GP practice infrastructure and the inherent close working relationship with top-down commissioners, has the propensity to change service provision without compromising the care of others. Providers' fixed costs can be addressed if, for example, a particular service for a large population (such as one or more localities) can be shifted from one arena to another, eg physiotherapy based in the community rather than the district general hospital. Thus issues of inequity should not arise. Providers will also have fewer purchasers to negotiate with.

Indeed, a commissioning agency acting with GP fundholders will have a greater purchasing leverage.

The commissioning process – locality input

A possible mechanism to feed locality commissioning intentions into the contracting and purchasing process of a commissioning agency/Health Authority is shown in Figure 16.5. This model is a GP practice-based locality mechanism.

It is envisaged that each locality has its own 'locality commissioning team' which draws together elected GP representatives, service users (perhaps represented through the Community Health Council, carers' groups etc), Social Services representatives and a purchasing agency locality Commissioner which liaises with providers (eg unit general managers, business/marketing managers of provider units and also the private and voluntary sectors) and with other Local Authority departments (eg cleaning and education). This locality commissioning team sends a representative to a purchasing group at the commissioning agency and thus locality commissioning is achieved through the commissioning agency contracting process.

In some areas, locality working is more top-down in its approach, with a locality manager from the Health Authority/commissioning agency visiting practices and feeding information thus gleaned into the contracting process.

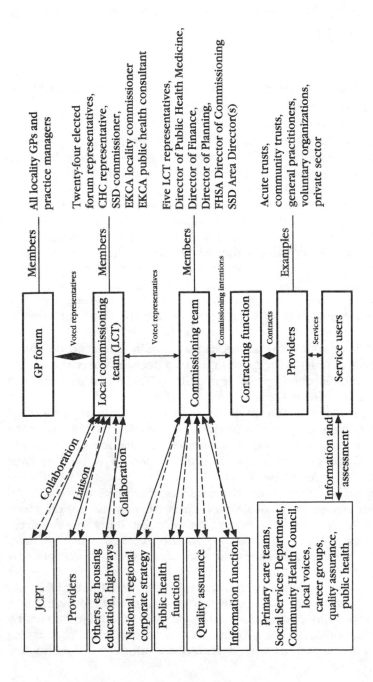

Figure 16.5: The locality commissioning concept

Examples of schemes in different parts of the country are given at the end of this chapter.

Locality commissioning and GP fundholding – a synergistic relationship

Why should the fundholding GP have any interest in locality commissioning? The fundholder has budgets, can vire between them and negotiate contracts. But the fundholder only purchases some 25–30% of all health care and has no purchasing access to the care provided by the Social Services Department. Even though the fundholder purchases much of the particularly 'contentious' health care (eg out-patient referrals, surgical procedures and the various therapy services), and perhaps is part of a multi-fundholder consortium (which can ameliorate the administrative load and augment purchasing leverage), the majority of commissioning is performed by the agencies and Health Authorities who will thus dictate the range of services which are available.

Without an additional mechanism, fundholders and non-fundholders alike have no more input into decisions over the scope, scale and distribution of this remaining 70–75% of services than before the NHS reforms.

Approximately 10% of health care is statutorily required to be provided (eg emergency services, certain elements of maternity services and communicable disease surveillance control), but even these 'ring-fenced' areas can be open to negotiation over mechanisms for delivery.

In Figure 16.6, block C represents that portion of the total health budget in a locality which is held by GP fundholders. Block A represents the budget set aside for 'statutorily required' services. Block B is therefore all that remains. The GP fundholder directly influences the use of resources represented by block C.

Through locality commissioning, the non-fundholder can directly influence the use of resources represented by block B and those services represented by block C which are utilized by non-fundholders. They can also influence the contracting process for services represented by block A. Fundholders

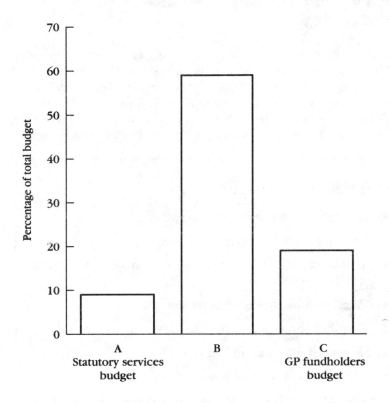

Figure 16.6: Proportions of available budgets in a locality for purchase of all health services.

joining a locality commissioning initiative will have similar influence over the use of resources represented by blocks A and B as the non-fundholder.

Where a Social Services department jointly commissions with local Health Authorities, then all 'locality commissioning' GPs can have influence over the commissioning of these services too.

Locality commissioning – possible disadvantages

Locality commissioning inevitably has advantages and disadvantages. *See* Figure 16.7. Its distinction is the overall alignment between commissioners, purchasers, providers and users of care services that is inherent in its make-up.

There is an increasing body of opinion that the advantages of locality commissioning outweigh the potential disadvantages

---

Advantages

- Community identity and participation.

- Team-building and bridge-building.

- Avoidance of duplication (both of management and service provision)

- Identification of lack of provision of care.

- Identification of inappropriate provision of care.

- Sharing of information and plans.

- Joint ownership of local strategy.

- Sensitivity to local issues and responsiveness, with flexibility.

- Balance of provision put in local perspective.

Disadvantages

- Fragmentation of top-down control.

- Possible increased bureaucracy and management costs (but less so than widespread GP fundholding).

- Some dis-economies of scale.

- Dissemination of control.

Figure 16.7: Issues for and against locality commissioning.

and as the concept develops nationally, with different models suiting different areas, with appropriate external appraisal the process should become further refined.

Examples of locality working

These are six examples of projects currently being undertaken, and while they are not all-inclusive, they indicate the wide range of models being tested.

- North Yorkshire (population 720,000); five local offices covering 24 'natural communities' (localities) grouped to match local authority boundaries.

- South-East London Health Authority (population 700,000); nine localities to be created, based on electoral ward boundaries but forming broadly homogeneous neighbourhoods. GP practices will be involved in the creation of localities, with Health Authority staff acting as co-ordinators.

- Stockport (population 295,000) has a four-tier structure:

Tier	Population	Services purchased
Neighbourhood	10,000	Primary care
Sector	50,000 primary care and some hospital services	Specialist
District	295,000 hospital services	Remaining
Consortium (not yet established)	1,000,000+ hospital services	Supra-district

Health strategy managers are to be appointed at sector level, liaising with neighbourhoods and different client groups, planning and purchasing for the neighbourhoods.

- Bath (practice-sensitive purchasing scheme). This is a voluntary scheme entailing a 'fair share' allocation of notional funds to GP practices (fundholders will have a notional budget for services not included in the fundholding scheme), with each practice expressing purchasing intentions within this notional budget which, if deemed reasonable by the Health Authority, are put into effect.

- Dorset (population 660,000); Six PATCHes centred on towns with populations of between 8,000 and 55,000. PATCHes are clustered into groups of two, three or four PATCH areas, each with a Health Authority-appointed co-ordinator. A steering group within each PATCH liaises with the community to identify needs and priorities. Contracts negotiated centrally are set against a PATCH budget.

- East Kent (population 700,000); initially divided into 15 localities based upon GP practice catchment populations. Following a six month pilot scheme, localities are in the process of being reconfigured to create five larger localities, but still defined by practice population. Input from GPs, CHC and Social Services, on a locality commissioning team (with ad hoc provider input of specialist expertise) will be fed into the contracting process in 1993 to be effected from 1 April 1994 as part of the next stage in this research project – the 'indicative scheme'. This will include the definition of 'locality spending profiles' which is hoped to lead to budget devolution to localities, probably via weighted capitation.

Summary

The concept of locality commissioning involves a 'local area', identifying and prioritizing its needs and commissioning the care thereby determined. This care is then purchased, by GP fundholders and also by commissioning agencies and FHSAs.

Locality commissioning is a mechanism which can align those best placed to assess needs at a local level (who have knowledge of local variations from the 'large area' norms but who currently work in small isolated teams) with top-down strategists and 'large area' commissioners of care.

Wide-reaching team-work and blending of top-down with

bottom-up working is a fundamental part of locality commissioning.

Locality commissioning is seen by some GPs as an alternative to fundholding, having all its advantages but not some of its perceived difficulties. However, localitity commissioning and GP fundholding are stable mates. They can work together harmoniously to enhance the care received by service users and have the potential in combination to create greater changes over wide areas of care.

17

Where to Turn to For Help

Antoinette Pirie

Managing a complex health care delivery and financing organization, such as that proposed by the fundholding scheme, calls for specialized personnel, management tools and techniques. The skills and expertise called for may not be currently available within practices. The Government acknowledges that GPs may have to look to other agencies for help and a fee set at the level which recognizes the 'management and other costs associated with participation' is included in the practice allocation.

A management allowance has been made to cover costs incurred during the preparatory year. Thereafter there is an annual allowance to cover fund management costs once the practice becomes fundholding.

The allocation could go towards:

- an extra member of staff to handle budget arrangements
- training for medical and ancillary staff
- locum cover
- professional consultancy services.

As part of the initial practice review undertaken before embarking upon fundholding a skills-need and training-needs analysis should be performed.

- Are the relevant skills and systems required for successful management of fundholding in place?
- If not, can they be developed in-house and what are the associated costs and timescales?

- If they need to be bought in where can the relevant expertise/training be found, and at what cost?

Consultancy services and training programmes are offered by a number of organizations to fill the perceived skill and knowledge gaps that the changes within general practice have uncovered.

The following is a list of organizations which offer specific services for general practice fundholders.

Bevan Ashford Solicitors
35 Colston Avenue
Bristol BS1 4TT
Tel: 0272 230111

The firm is one of the largest practices in the country offering legal advice to health service clients via a network of offices. With a longstanding presence in this area they are well placed to advise and assist on the new issues and opportunities now facing the service.

Capita Group plc
Great West House
Great West Road
Brentford TW8 9DF
Tel: 081 560 9922

Offer general consultancy and business planning services and are keen to develop their work with fundholders.

Centre for Health Planning and Management
University of Keele
Keele ST5 5BG
Tel: 0782 583191

The Centre is a well established multidisciplinary institute concentrating on both academic and applied health service studies. With over 40 full-time faculty staff, its portfolio of activities includes teaching, research and consultancy/advisory work.

The Centre offers a range of executive courses, workshops and seminars either on the Keele campus or on site with the client. The broad disciplines covered include:

- general management and management development
- health policy issues
- information and communications.

The Centre does not offer a specific fundholding package and their consultants would work on an individual project basis. Areas covered by the Centre's consultants include:

- information – advising on appropriate data and information bases for planning at the small area level
- finance – designing information systems that link together finance, manpower and activity data
- primary health care – analysis of GP out-patient referrals
- medical audit – quality assurance in the primary and secondary care sectors.

Centre for Health Services Management
Leicester Business School
Leicester LE1 9BH
Tel: 0533 577243 Ext. 7222

The HSM Centre has developed a package specifically aimed at fund-holders. The programme is an extended version of a workshop on financial management and business planning that was sponsored by BUPA. The one day modules cover:

- financial management
- business planning
- information needs for fundholders.

The Centre also offers a 'tailor-made' consultancy service.

Coopers Lybrand Deloitte
Plumtree Court
London EC4A 4HT
Tel: 071 583 5000

The increased budgeting and accounting/purchasing decisions being placed upon GPs by the recent changes in the NHS have led the firm to think about GPs' needs. The firm can provide the following services for GPs:

- internal audit/review

- partnership accounts audit

- systems advice/review

- small-scale general consulting

- project management eg new premises

- fundraising and loan advice.

Cygnet Health Care plc
Godden Green Clinic
Sevenoaks
Kent TN15 OJR
Tel: 0732 63491

The company was incorporated in 1987 to develop and manage short-stay acute psychiatric hospitals and private nursing homes up and down the country. The same private psychiatric units have each gained a reputation for providing the highest quality of nursing care and hotel facilities. Specialized treatment and therapy programmes are devised individually for patients, while the comfortable environment and ambiance in themselves help promote swift recovery.

For fundholding GPs, a non-exclusive Service Agreement is now available which enables a defined range of services to be purchased within the scope of the budget. This provides a realistic alternative for referrals, within a framework of agreed quality standards and competitive prices.

The Department for Enterprise (DTI)
Bridge Place
88–89 Eccleston Square
London SW1V 1PT
Tel: 071 627 7800

A number of fundholding practices have turned .to the DTI Enterprise Initiative for consultancy assistance. The consultancy service is available twice, for different projects, and groups with fewer than 500 employees are eligible. The DTI will pay up to two thirds of the cost of specialist help for projects lasting between five and 15 days in the following areas:

- marketing
- design
- quality
- manufacturing systems
- business planning
- financial and information systems.

The final two initiatives are of particular interest to potential fundholders. The initiatives offer a low-cost method for practices to obtain specific consultancy advice. It is particularly suitable for practices that are basically well managed and have identified weaknesses in specific areas covered by the scheme. It would not be suitable for practices needing more widespread help.

Andrew Donaldson: management, development and training
3 Tudor Gardens
Stony Stafford
Milton Keynes MK11 1HX
Tel: 0908 565020

This organization has over 25 years' experience in NHS management, latterly planning district services in the Oxford Region, involving several new health and medical centres in Milton Keynes. They provide wide-ranging consultancy advice including purchaser and provider contracts, medical audit and management training.

Granville Sansom Personnel and Management Consultancy
The Phoenix
Napsbury Hospital
London Colney
St Albans AL2 1BN
Tel: 0727 821530

The firm has wide experience of working with general practices.

- Management support to fundholding and non-fundholding practices including business planning, personnel issues, staff training and internal reviews.
- PGEA approved training sessions covering business planning, marketing, contract negotiation, costing and budget setting.
- PGEA approved study tours to The Netherlands.

Work with fundholding practices in particular includes:

- recruitment and selection of practice business managers and practice staff
- business planning support and training
- development and implementation of practice procedures and management structures
- financial analysis of practices including assessment of target performance
- liaison with the FHSA on behalf of practices.

Healthcare Consultancy Services
27A Bancroft
Hitchin
Herts SG5 1JW
Tel: 0462 452997

Healthcare Consultancy Services (N. Ireland)
2 Mill Heights
Kircubbin
Co. Down BT 22 2ON
Tel: 02477 38660

Healthcare Consultancy Services provides a service specifically tailored to fundholding and prospective fundholding practices. The founders of Healthcare Consultancy Services have extensive experience of preparation for and running all aspects of fundholding.

Healthcare Consultancy Services has FHSA fundholding systems and consortium management experience specifically mentioned in Professor Glennerster's report 'A Foothold for Fundholding' for the King's Fund Institute.

Healthcare Consultancy Services can build upon the existing practice structure to ensure the smooth introduction and implementation of fundholding and provide a personal and individual service tailored specifically to the needs of each practice.

Healthcare Consultancy Services can provide a back-up service in the event of unforeseen absences through sickness or other reasons. They provide the following services to fundholding practices.

- data collection

- practice management organization

- business planning

- fund negotiation

- contract specification and structure

- contract negotiations

- fundholding computer systems set-up

- contract monitoring

- budget monitoring

- monthly financial closure and reporting

- year-end financial closure and reporting

- financial audit to ensure system accuracy.

Health Services Management Centre
University of Birmingham
Park House
40 Edgbaston Park Road
Birmingham B15 2RT
Tel: 021 414 3344

The Centre responded early to the GP funding initiative and held an initial one day conference in 1990 on some of the major issues involved. Following this a series of one and two day workshops were arranged for GPs, FHSAs, units and DHAs. The topics covered by the Centre include:

- business planning and negotiating skills for GPs

- budgetary management for GPs

- marketing hospital and community services to fundholders

- assessing the impact of fundholding on patients.

Mercedes Kelly-Madden
General Practice Fundholding Consultancy
133 Old London Road
Hastings TN 35 5LY
Tel: 0424 422491

The King's Fund
14 Palace Court
London W2
and
The King's Fund Centre
126 Albert Street
London NW1 7NF
Tel: 071 267 6111

The King's Fund Centre provides a base for the Fund on health services development. The objective is to support innovations in the NHS and related organizations and to encourage the uptake of new ideas and good practice in healthcare. They offer a variety of seminars and courses of direct relevance to fundholders.

Management Advisory Service
11 Royal Crescent
Cheltenham GL50 3DA
Tel: 0242 519908

MAS worked with two RHAs in the run up to fundholding. Their initial work was concerned with developing action plans for the first wave practices using fact sheets and holding workshops.

As well as helping with contracting issues such as quality measures and monitoring arrangements MAS can also provide help in the areas of data collection, training and publicity.

NHS Training and Studies Centre
Cold Bath Road
Harrogate HG2 ONF
Tel: 0423 505 681

The Centre operates from within the NHS Training Authority as an internal consultancy and development resource for the NHS and NHS Management Board. They aim to run events which are predominantly for senior staff in the service. The courses, workshops and seminars are typically tailor-made to suit a diagnosed need.

The following courses, for which PGEA accreditation has been applied for, are of relevance to fund-holders:

- medical audit programme

- managing change in general practice

- time and priorities in general practice

- an audit cycle for general practice.

Pannell Kerr Forster
Pannell House
Park Street
Guildford GU1 4HN
Tel: 0483 64646

Pannell Kerr Forster has over 50 years' experience of dealing with the accountancy and financial affairs of members of the medical profession. The firm has responded to the fundholding initiative and offers the following services to fund-holding GPs:

- the Department of Health (DoH) Helpline. In order to assist practices and managers in understanding the Manual of Accounts and to provide immediate explanation, the DoH invited Pannell Kerr Forster to set up a telephone helpline: 0483 573853

- help with the preparation of annual fundholding accounts for the FHSA

- help with the production of practice business plans

- help with computer services in conjunction with the GP computer supplier AAH Meditel

- recruitment of specialist staff

- advice on management of savings accounts.

Price Waterhouse (Office of Healthcare Services)
Southwark Towers
London Bridge Street
London SE1 9SY
Tel: 071 939 3000

Price Waterhouse, through its healthcare management consulting arm, the Office of Healthcare Services, with offices in London, Bristol and Leeds, offers a full range of assistance to GP fundholders. Services include:

- advice on information technology from system specification to implementation

- advice on negotiating contracts with provider units including the development of quality standards

- assistance with management of practice costs

- help with the analysis and interpretation of casemix information.

In addition they are also able to offer tax advice through the tax branch of the firm.

Ramsay Brown and Partners
Ramsay House
825 High Road
Finchley
London N12 8UB
Tel: 081 445 3351

Ramsay Brown and Partners specialize in the finances of medical practitioners, and currently service more than 500 GPs, from single-handed to ten partner fundholding practices. Both partners, Laurence Slavin and Stuart Singer, write and lecture extensively on the finances of GPs.

Peter Stanley Associates
Birch House
Startley
Nr Chippenham SN15 5HG
Tel: 0249 721172

A medium-sized consultancy practice which specializes exclusively in healthcare. Peter Stanley Associates work throughout the NHS with both purchasers and providers. The firm carries out thorough reviews of practices to identify strengths and weaknesses *vis à vis* fundholding potential. Specific areas would include:

- analysis of current patient referrals and options for change

- providing a detailed 'profile of need for hospital services'

- assessing the practice business including information and accounting requirements, management and staffing structure

- roles of the partners in the management of the practice

- team building and management development

- evaluating appointment systems

- advising on purchaser specifications for hospital and community services.

Peter Stanley Associates are able to match their services to meet the specific requirements of individual practices including the provision of on-going support to provide regular 'as and when' advice.

Touche Ross
Hill House
1 Little New Street
London EC4A 3TR
Tel: 071 936 3000

Touche Ross and Spicer Oppenheim merged in 1990. The health-care practices of the two firms were complementary – Touche Ross specialized in working at RHA and DHA level and Spicer and Oppenheim had strong links with the primary care sector.

Their consultants have worked in all parts of the health service from the Department of Health to individual purchaser and provider units, FHSAs and general practice.

VAMP Health Ltd
The Bread Factory
la Broughton Street
London SW8 3QT
Tel: 071 498 1330

Over 450 VAMP practices are now using the VAMP Fund Holding System, across all waves, and with a variety of hardware configurations.

- Full DoH accreditation, plus many enhancements.

- Regionally-based trainers are all ex-practice managers and GPs.

- Able to electronically link to any clinical system.

Wilter Associates Management Consultants
Willow Court
Marsham Lane
Gerrards Cross SL9 8HD
Tel: 0753 890359

A group of six consultants with backgrounds in both the public and private sector. All the consultants have worked in the NHS either as doctors, nurses or managers. They aim to help organizations manage change whatever its basis, be it: IT, financial systems, people issues, crisis etc. The group offer a personalized service working with their clients to help them acquire skills and competencies. In all their projects they emphasize the 'soft' issues. By a combination of facilitation, creative management and organization development techniques they aim to help organizations make the cultural adjustment to the 'change catalyst' as well as designing and implementing the more obvious 'hard' solutions.

The following is a list of the other firms whose fundholding software has passed DoH conformance testing:

AAH Meditel Ltd
Rigby Hall
Rigby Lane
Bromsgrove B60 2EW
Tel: 0527 579414

AMC Ltd
Clarendon House
The Bridal Path
Watford WD2 4AA
Tel: 0923 255740

Anglia Consultants (MTECH and AMSYS)
The Old Brewery House
The Market Square
Reepham NR10 4JJ
Tel: 0603 871999

Micro-doc
Hollowbrook House
Lydgate Lane
Sheffield S10 5SH
Tel: 04336 30497

Update Computers Ltd
19–30 Alfred Place
London WC1E 7EA
Tel: 071 580 8121

18

Common Questions Asked

Mercedes Kelly

Practices applying to join the fundholding scheme usually have numerous questions. We have compiled a list of those most commonly asked.

Question: How much reimbursement can the practice expect if they need to upgrade their computer system and buy the fundholding software?

Answer: Full reimbursement of costs can be made in respect of any fundholding software package which has successfully completed conformance testing. Payments are also made for training costs associated with any of the packages.

System purchase costs: In the case of fundholding practices, the level of reimbursement will be 75% of the actual net price of specific hardware.

Upgrading costs: Subject to the availability of funds, payment, less any deduction in respect of private income from the sale of anonymized data, will be made in respect of a proportion of the costs incurred by the practitioner, partnership or group practice in upgrading an existing computer system for the use of the practice. This includes both hardware and software costs. An existing computer system may be owned, rented or leased.

Question: What additional management expertise is needed to manage and organize the fund?

Answer: While many practice managers already in post feel confident to manage a fund, experience is showing that practices who appoint a full-time fund manager with no other practice commitments operate more successfully. In the preparatory year this person can be paid on a pro-rata, part-time basis from the management allowance. When the practice has completed the preparatory year and the management allowance is paid in full the position can then become full-time at the appropriate salary. With those practices which group together to form a consortia or co-operative, more than one management allowance will be available in the preparatory year and, therefore, it would be possible to recruit a full-time manager from the beginning of the preparatory year.

Question: How do we find out about our patients on waiting lists?

Answer: All providers will now be in a position to give a practice, by GP, the names of those patients on waiting lists either by consultant or specialty. A method of cross checking these is to put up a simple poster in the waiting room asking those patients who are on waiting lists to register at reception and cross-check.

Question: How do we find out about those patients who are now chronically ill and attend hospital out-patients?

Answer: The most effective way to locate these patients at present (as there are no records as yet for chronic attenders at out-patient clinics) is to print a clear notice asking those patients attending hospital diabetic, asthma clinics etc to advise reception. A database can be built up from this information allowing GPs to recall these patients and assess whether it is still necessary for them to be seen in the hospital-based clinic.

Question: Where do we get provider costs and who do we contact?

Answer: All providers now issue price lists directly to fund-holders or on request to prospective fundholders. Attached to these are names and telephone numbers of the people responsible for contracts for each directorate. If this is not available then your FHSA will advise on who to contact.

Question: What happens if we overspend our budget?

Answer: The FHSA is responsible for monitoring your expenditure and the fundholding software prints an end of each month return which enables the FHSA finance directors to project fund's expenditure. If an overspend looks like happening then the FHSA will give the necessary guidance to bring you back on course.

Question: What can we spend our savings on?

Answer: Savings cannot be identified until the end of each financial year following completion of the practice budget annual accounts. Should savings be accrued they may be spent for the benefit of your patients on:

- paying for additional staff or hospital services
- improving facilities for patients
- providing additional medical equipment.

You are not obliged to make savings and if you do you may not carry over one sum for more than four years.

Appendix 1

Elective Surgical Procedures Covered by the Fundholding Scheme

Code procedure description

OPGS 4th revision operations codes

Ophthalmology

A01	Operations for squint	C31 to C35
A02	Chalazion operation	C12
A03	Pterygium operation	C39.1
A04	Operations for ectropion, entropion and ptosis	C15.1 C15.2 C18
A05	Operations for glaucoma	C59 C60 C61 C62 C66.3 C66.4
A06	Operations for obstruction of the nasolacrimal duct	C25 C27
A07	Extraction of cataract with/out intra-ocular implant	C71 C72 C74 C75
A08	Corneal graft	C46
A09	Laser treatment for vascular retinopathies	C82.1

Ear, nose and throat

B01	Myringotomy	D15.3
B02	Insertion of grommet	D15.1
B03	Mastoidectomy	D10 except D10.5
B04	Stapedectomy	D17.1 D17.2
B05	Tympanoplasty	D14
B06	Labyrinthectomy	D26.2 D26.3
B07	Septoplasty	E03.4 to E03.9
B08	Sub-mucous resection of septum	E03.1

B09	Polypectomy	E08.1
B10	Ethmoidectomy	E14.1 to E14.4
B11	Turbinectomy	E04.2
B12	Cautery of lesion of nasal mucosa	E05.1
B13	Puncture of maxillary antrum with wash-out	E13.6
B14	Drainage of maxillary sinus	E12.2 to E13.1
B15	Exploration of frontal sinus	E14.9
B16	Tonsillectomy	F34
B17	Adenoidectomy	E20.1
B18	Pharyngoscopy	E24 E25
B19	Laryngoscopy	E34 E35 E36
B20	Laryngectomy	E29
B21	Block dissection	T85.1

Thoracic

C01	Bronchoscopy with/out biopsy	E48 E49 E50 E51
C02	Biopsy/excision of lesions of lung or bronchus	E46.2 to E46.9 E47.1 E55 E59.1 to E59.3
C04	Lobectomy	E54
C05	Pneumonectomy	E54

Cardiovascular

| D01 | Operations for valvular or ischaemic heart diseases (excluding neonatal and infant surgery) | K25 to K35 K40 to K51 |

General surgery

E01	Partial thyroidectomy	B12.1 B12.2 B08.2 to B08.9
E02	Total thyroidectomy	B08.1
E03	Thyroidectomy of aberrent thyroid gland	B09.1 B09.2

E04	Operation on salivary gland and ducts	F44 to F58
E05	Operations on para-thyroid glands	B14 B16
E06	Oesophagoscopy with/out endoscopic procedures	G14 to G19
E07	Dilation of oesophagus	G18.2 G18.3 G15.2 G15.3
E08	Operation on varices of of the oesophagus	G10 G14.4 G17.4
E09	Gastrectomy partial or total	G27 G28
E10	Vagotomy with/out other operative procedure	A27 G33.1 G40.1 G40.3
E11	Endoscopy with/out endoscopic procedures	G43 G44 G45 G54 G55 G62 G64 G65 G79 G80
E12	Laparoscopy with/out biopsy	T42 T43
E13	Excision of lesion of small intestine	G50 G53.1 G59 G63.1 G70 G78
E14	Partial colectomy	H06 to H11
E15	Total colectomy	H04 H05
E16	Sigmoidoscopy with/out biopsy/polypectomy	H23 to H28
E17	Colonoscopy with/out biopsy/polypectomy	H20 H21 H22
E18	Exteriorization of bowel	H15
E19	Repair of prolapsed rectum	H35 H36 H42
E20	Operations for anal fissures and fistula	H56.4
E21	Excision of rectum	H33
E23	Pilonidal sinus	H59 H60
E24	Dilation of anal sphincter	H54
E25	Haemorrhoidectomy	H51 H52 H53
E26	Operations on the gall bladder	J18 to J26
E27	Operations on the bile ducts	J27 to J52

E28	Mastectomy	B27
E29	Excision/biopsy of breast lesion	B28 B32
E30	Repair of inguinal hernia	T19 T20 T21
E31	Repair of femoral hernia	T22 T23
E32	Repair of incisional hernia	T25 T26
E33	Varicose veins stripping/ligation	L85 L86 L87
E34	Surgical treatment of ingrowing toenail	S64 S68 S70.1
E35	Excision/biopsy of skin or subcutaneous tissue	{ S05 S06 S09 S10.2 S11.2 S13 S14 S15
E36	Lymph node excision/biopsy	T87

Genitourinary

F01	Cystoscopy with/out destruction of bladder lesion	M42 M44 M45 M76 M77
F02	Dilation of urethra/urethrotomy	M76.4 M81 M58 M79 M76.3 M75
F03	Urethroplasty	M73
F04	Open repair	M73.4
F05	Prostatectomy open or TUR	M61 M65
F06	Excision of hydrocele	N11
F07	Orchidopexy	N08 N09
F08	Male sterilization	N17
F09	Circumcision	N30
F10	Varicocele	N19
F11	Removal of ureteric or renal calculus	M09 M26 M27 M28 M06.1 M23.1
F12	Lithotripsy	M14 M31
F13	Nephrectomy	M02 M03

Gynaecology

G01	Oophorectomy/salping-oophorectomy	{ Q22.1 Q22.3 Q23.1 Q23.2 { Q23.5 Q23.6 Q24.1 Q24.3
G02	Ovarian cystectomy	Q43.2
G03	Wedge resection of ovary	Q43.1
G04	Female sterilization	Q35 Q36 Q27 Q28
G05	Patency tests of Fallopian tubes	Q39.9 Q41
G06	Hysterectomy abdominal/vaginal	Q07 Q08
G07	Myomectomy	Q09.2
G08	D and C with/out polypectomy	Q10.3
G09	Cone biopsy	Q03.1 Q03.3
G10	Colposcopy with/out biopsy of cervix	Q02 Q03.4 to Q03.9 P27.3
G11	Anterior or posterior repair	P22 P23 P24 P13.2 P13.3
G12	Vulvectomy/partial vulvectomy/vulval biopsy	P05 except P05.3 P06 P09.1
G13	Marsupialization of Bartholin's cyst/abcess	P03.2 P05.3
G14	Diagnostic laparoscopy with/out biopsy	Q39 Q50
G16	EUA	Q55.2
G17	Hysterectomy/endometrial resection	

Orthopaedics

H01	Operation on inter-vertebral discs	V29 to V35 V52
H02	Therapeutic lumbar epidural injection	A52.1
H03	Arthroplasty/revision arthoplasty of hip or knee	W37 to W42 W46 W47 W48
H04	Removal of implanted substance from bone	W35.3

H05	Upper tibial osteotomy	W12
H06	Arthroscopy with/out other intra-articular procedures	W82 to W88
H07	Intra-articular injections	W90
H08	Meniscectomy	W70 W82
H09	Corrections of hammer toe etc	W59.5
H10	Dupuytren's contracture	T52.1 T52.2
H11	Carpal tunnel decompression	A65.1
H12	Release of trigger finger	T72.3
H13	Excision of ganglion	T59 T60
H14	Aspiration/excision of bursa	T62.1 to T62.5
H15	Osteotomy for hallux valgus/rigidus	W57.1 W15

Appendix 2

Extension of the Hospital and Community Health Services Elements of the GP Fundholding Scheme From 1 April 1993

The following is based on the current guidance from the NHSME, the implementation of which may vary from location to location depending on local policy and the delivery of services.

The guidance is for the first year of the community extensions, 1993/94, and may well be amended or extended prior to the commencement of the second year on 1 April 1994.

Department of Health

Guidance   EL (92) 48
Supplementary guidance   HSG (92) 53

Services

- District nursing.
- Health visiting.
- Chiropody.
- Dietetics.
- All community and out-patient mental health services.
- Mental health counselling.
- Health services for people with a learning disability.
- Referrals made by health visitors, district nurses and community mental handicap nurses.

Possible Problems

- Poor information held by provider.

- The referral source may be difficult to identify.

- Practice referrals known but tariff in face-to-face contacts.

- Practices receive minimal funding based on previous activity levels within the NHS (a particular problem where the existing service is practice-based and funded from health promotion via the FHSA).

Mental health services

Services

All mental health service, provided by out-patient or community, mental health units.

Inclusions

- Services to special groups, eg children, elderly people and substance abusers.

- Mental health counselling including and psychotherapy.

- CPN services – where CPNs are attached to or provide services directly to fundholding practices.

- Referrals by CPNs to other services within the fundholding scheme.

- Referrals by other members of the PHCT to mental health services.

- All GP and PHCT referrals for child and adolescent mental health services irrespective of where they are delivered.

- Psychology services, currently provided outside the multi-disciplinary CMHT to include non-psychiatric referrals:
    - trauma care
    - psychological aspects of medical care
    - group approaches to mental health.

Exclusions

- Assessments made under the Mental Health Act.
- Self-referrals.
- Voluntary agencies (providing services).
- Regional/supra regional and highly specialized services.
- In-patients.
- Services provided by SSDs.
- Social care and accommodation costs of hostel care.
- Day and respite care.
- Child guidance services funded by non-NHS agencies.

Obligations

- Fund all mental health services provided by out-patient and community mental health units.
- Fully operate the 'care programme' approach.
- Take account of local clinical protocols which may require referrals to be made to the CMHT.

Options

- Commission services by means of a referral led contract.
- Commission direct access services provided by CPNs.
- Enter agreement with other commissioners (including DHAs) to purchase jointly.

Although regulations will not compel fundholders to place a contract with an NHS community or mental health unit for these particular services, the delivery of psychiatric services through the NHS mental health team with its strong ties with SSDs is seen as central to good practice.

Future plans

It is hoped that protocols and referral criteria will be developed further so that there is a shared understanding of referrals.

Possible problems

- Terminology
    - in-patient   - excluded
    - out-patient   - included
    - day care   - excluded
    - ? rehabilitation
    - ? living skills
    - ? therapy sessions
    - ? support groups
    - ? drop-in centres.
- Invoicing by providers.
- Role of social workers and other local authority employees.
- Likely implications of any planned closures of long stay units.
- Shared care with consultant psychiatrist.
- Identifying current activity in all areas covered by the extension.
- Possible overlap and double counting of out-patient attendances already covered by the scheme.
- Price per referral to team vs individual tariffs per team member.

Services for those with learning disabilities

Services

All non in-patient services provided by the NHS for people with a learning disability, including:

- CMH nursing

- CPN
- occupational therapy
- counselling
- psychology
- physiotherapy
- speech therapy

Inclusions

- Out-patient treatment.
- Community-based services provided by specialist professionals.
- Services provided by CMHT members themselves.
- Referrals from CPNs and CMH nurses.
- From PHCT members including community nurses.
- Referrals for health care from other agencies, eg local authorities and voluntary organizations.

Exclusions

- In-patient services.
- Self-referrals.
- Day and respite care.
- Tertiary referrals to regional/supraregional services.

Obligations

- To be funded for the whole package of health care provided for patients with learning difficulties.

Options

- Commission service for patients with learning difficulties by means of a referral-led contract.

- Commission services on a fixed-price, non-attributable basis.

- Enter an agreement with other commissioners (including DHAs) to purchase jointly.

Possible problems

- Where the service has transferred to and is led by SSDs.

- Providers may find it difficult to collect sufficient data.

- Services are not necessarily requested by GPs.

- Absence of referral protocols involving:
  - health
  - SSDs
  - voluntary bodies
  - GPs
  - parents and family.

- Associated problems – disturbed and challenging behaviour.

- Client identification.

- Implications of other guidance, eg health services for people with learning disabilities (mental handicap) (HSG(92)42).

Dietetics

Services

This is a comprehensive service which offers nutrition and dietetic education, clinical support and information.

Inclusions

- Referrals from fundholders or persons acting on behalf of the practice.

- Clinical sessions or health promotion activities exclusively for the fundholders practice population.

Exclusions

- Public health duties, eg health road shows, careers conventions, talks to voluntary groups etc.

- Student training.

- Activities for other commissioners, eg dietetic input into hospital-based services.

- Initial and follow-up visits resulting from all consultant referrals.

Obligations

- Include dietetic services as part of the extension to the GP fundholding scheme from 1 April 1993.

- Fund practices according to the level of previous NHS referrals made by GPs or practice staff.

Options

- Contract with NHS providers.

- Contract with other providers.

- Employ staff direct.

- Vire resources into dietetic services.

Chiropody

Services

- Skin and nail problems.

- Structural conditions.

- Biomechanical evaluation.

- Minor surgery.

- Ambulatory surgery (podiatric surgery).

- Child foot health.

- Appliance clinics.

Community and Hospital-based

Inclusions

- Referrals made by GPs, district nurses and health visitors of a fundholding practice.

- Referrals made by Local Authority Social Services.

- Follow-up community-based care as a result of hospital referral for specialities such as diabetes and rheumatology.

- Foot care assistants.

Exclusions

- Treatment arising from needs identified during school screening.

- Public health duties, eg health road shows, career conventions, foot health talks etc.

- Student training activity, eg placements.

- Activity occurring for other commissioners sub-contracted by other provider units, eg chiropody input in a hospital-based diabetic clinic.

- Self-referrals (for the present).

Obligations

- Chiropody services must be included as part of the extension to the GP Fundholding Scheme from 1 April 1993.

- Practices funded according to the level of previous NHS referrals made by GPs or practice staff.

Options

- Contract with NHS providers.

- Employ staff direct.

- Vire resources into chiropody

Possible problems

- Obtaining accurate activity data on which to base a budget.

- Self-referrals account for over 75% of referrals.

- Poor information held by provider.

- Practice may know referrals, but provider tariff in face-to-face contacts.

- Long-term care (in excess of contract period).

- Practices receive minimal funding based on previous activity levels within the NHS (a particular problem where the existing service is practice-based and funded from health promotion via the FHSA).

- Directly employs staff,
    - appropriately trained and experienced staff
    - opportunities for continuing professional development

Community nursing services

Inclusions

- All health visiting and district nursing services for the practice population, irrespective of whether the staff are attached or locality-based.

- Referrals made by health visitors and district nurses.

- Referrals made to health visitors and district nurses by agencies outside the NHS (eg LEA or SSD).

- Weekend services provided by community nurses attached to the practice.

Exclusions

- Public health element of health visitors
    - contact tracing
    - port health
    - health education
    - district wide schemes
    - market stalls/road shows
    - communicable disease work

    } possible definition is any service involving population wider than the practice population

- Specialist nursing services
    - stoma care
    - continence promotion
    - diabetes
    - Macmillan nursing

    } not normally based in PHCTs

- Twilight and night-nursing services.

- Community practice teachers (H grade).Fundholders should not be funded for the cost of teaching in practice. Where CPTs are attached to fundholding practices, the difference in their salary, ie, H-G, should be costed as an overhead of all G grades.

- Services provided by health visitors specifically to travellers, the homeless and those not registered with a GP.

Budget setting

- The baseline should be the current level of services provided to each fundholding practice measured in whole-time equivalents

- Consider the current skill mix and grades of staff.

- Account for any planned changed.

Obligations

- Contract with an established NHS provider only.

- Contract for at least the current level of services.

- Place fixed-price non-attributable contracts (ie not volume-sensitive; costs and referral statistics are non-attributable to individual patients).

Constraints

- Staff cannot be employed direct.
- A private nursing agency cannot be used.

Options

- Transfer funds from other elements of the fundholding budget into community nursing.
- Initiate negotiations around skill mix.
- Employ additional practice nurses where funds are released.
- Use alternative NHS providers.
- Vary the number of NHS providers.

Possible problems

- Establishing the current level of service: is it the funded establishment or staff in post?
- Identifying the services: are they included or excluded, are they the DHA responsibility or absorbed as an overhead cost?
- Identifying the purchaser responsible for:
  - community practice teaching
  - specialist nursing, pain control
  - aids store (? funded from joint finance)
  - incontinence consumables
  - Children Act
  - specialist advice on child protection
  - clerical/managerial/professional support
  - aids and appliances
  - equipment
  - eontinuing education and in-service training.
- Impact of central initiatives (eg on waiting lists).
- Development plans.
- Community care plans.
- Regional strategies and priorities.

- Implications of change in the practice list size.
- Statutory functions.
- Providing services from non-recurring funds (virements and savings).

Future plans

- Develop protocols to ensure all referrals made on behalf of the practice are recognized and agreed in advance.
- Develop information systems as community activity is based on the number of patient contacts.
- Establish capitation-based methodology for community nursing.

Summary

1 Avoid misunderstandings on the scope of the service and which purchaser is responsible.

2 Identify the goods and services absorbed as overhead costs.

3 Choose the most appropriate contract.

4 Collect data to ensure all services are funded and purchased from 1 April 1994.

5 Allow for planned developments of the scheme.

6 Provide for change in the purchase of services or the type of contract in subsequent years.

7 Develop protocols which enable the practice to manage and control its fundholding resources, including the effective use of fundholding software.

Index